WITHDRAWN

DOCTORS

WHO

SAVED LIVES

By LYNN and GRAY POOLE

ILLUSTRATED

———————————

DODD, MEAD & COMPANY

NEW YORK

Library of Congress Catalog Card Number: 66-20318
Printed in the United States of America
by The Cornwall Press, Inc., Cornwall, N. Y.

We dedicate this book to
Webster Laurence Marxer, M.D.
physician and friend

Contents

Illustrations

xi]

Frederick Grant Banting

Alexander Fleming

Howard Walter Florey

Ernst Boris Chain

*All illustrations are used through the courtesy of the
National Library of Medicine*

Heresy! The Rebirth
of Knowledge

Europe in the late fifteenth century was seething with intellectual ferment. By the middle of the sixteenth century, there was a newly established era marked by a rebirth of knowledge, a revival of learning, and destined to be known as the Renaissance. No single milestone of progress dates the Renaissance. It evolved from exploration and invention, from creative thinking in the arts, letters, religion, philosophy, and all sciences. Advancement in medical research and therapy matched other progress of the time.

Open-minded scholars sought new areas of learning and new interpretations of ancient thinking. Man, center of his own universe, created the humanistic approach to all fields of thought and action. After 1456, when Johann Gutenberg completed the first Bible printed in movable type, it was possible for treatises

containing revolutionary ideas to be circulated widely;
these were disseminated with speed and accuracy. In
1492, Christopher Columbus discovered the New
World and opened the way for other explorers to follow: John Cabot to Canada, Amerigo Vespucci to the
Americas, Vasco da Gama to India. Many men traveled
from European seaport centers to strange and exciting
distant lands in search of trade and knowledge. The
broadening of world horizons paralleled the expansion
of man's thinking.

Religious beliefs were re-examined. Savonarola,
Martin Luther, John Calvin, and others, flaunting the
enervating power of the Church, fomented new doc-
trines and dared to demand religious freedom for all.
Authorities ordered the burning at the stake of men
branded as heretics: Bishops Ridley and Latimer at
Oxford, and Archbishop Cranmer at Canterbury. In
1560, twelve hundred Huguenots were hanged at Am-
boise, France, for the crime of thinking for themselves
about doctrinal matters, for their insistence on following the dictates of their own minds, hearts, and souls.

Heresy was the keynote of the times. It spurred men
of stature who were discontent with the crushing weight
of religious, civil, and intellectual domination. They
revolted against dogmatic tradition that was unchang-
ing because men in power feared the loss of that power.
The word "heresy" is derived from the Greek *hairesis,*
meaning the action of taking choice. In the fifteenth
century, those holding vengeant power brooked no

change. Anyone who held religious opinion contrary
to established dogma of the Church was a heretic. In
secular areas, heresy was the act of "taking or making a
choice or a dissent from a dominant thing or opinion
held to be unalterably true." Men, influenced by the
new humanism and sparked by Greek thought, com-
mitted heresy not only against the Church but in every
field of human thought and every facet of human en-
deavor.

In earlier day, St. Augustine wrote, "Do you think
that heresies could have arisen from a few beggarly little
souls? Only great, uncommon men with uncommon
ideas have brought forth heresies. They did it because
they dared to believe and to stand by their well-founded
beliefs."

Heretical artists of the Renaissance knowingly broke
the Church rule that the human body was sacred and
not to be despoiled. Seeking new ways to study the human figure in order to portray it more faithfully, the
artists secured cadavers that they dissected secretly in
order to better understand the interrelation of various
parts of the anatomy. The result of their study was the
creation of a new art that was a high point of the age.
And the artists opened the way for medical men seeking
information about the bodies of their living patients.
Doctors also had to do their work on dead bodies in the
dark and with utmost secrecy.

While a medical student at Padua, Italy, Copernicus

was fired with the ideas of freedom of thought and began the studies that he carried forward at the University of Kraków in Poland, his homeland. Astronomy became the prime subject of research for Copernicus and, after extensive study, he theorized that the sun was at the center of the universe. That revolutionary theory was violently condemned by Church and State.

The masses and tyrannical leaders are always suspicious of an individual who thinks for himself and dares to put forth a new idea that threatens the comfort of life as it is. Yet every generation must remake itself, establishing its own values, circumstances, habits, and limitations. Intellectual, social, political, and religious processes, becoming obsolete, fail to serve contemporary needs. But how the human animal resents essential change and fights it off. Men who dare to suggest change are pilloried by word and deed. In his fifth Olympic Ode, Pindar wrote that those ". . . always attendant on valor, work and substance struggle to win the end, veiled in constant danger; but when men succeed, even their neighbors think them wise."

Medical men of the Renaissance who took their place in world history did not always triumph in their own day or even know that by the extent of their contributions they would earn the right to be called "wise."

In his own time, Valerius Cordus traveled far, gathering medical facts and preparing the first pharmaceutic formulary to receive legal sanction. His formulary guided physicians throughout the civilized world of that age as they prescribed treatment for patients. Cordus discovered a volatile liquid known as *ether,* but, while he noted its sleep-producing qualities, application of ether as anesthesia was to wait until October 16, 1846, when William T. G. Morton first used it for painless surgery in Boston.

François Rabelais of France, while reading in the original Greek the works of the fourth century B.C. physician Hippocrates, discovered many errors in existing translations. Other men whose curiosity led them to new examinations of medical documents in the Greek language also found previous translations to be faulty. Errors in medical textbooks derived from the Greeks were perpetrated by Arabian and Hebrew translators. Leonicenus found many mistakes in what had been considered standard translations of the works of Hippocrates, Aristotle, Pliny, and Galen. By painstaking study and comparison, he found places where the translators had purposely mistranslated the ancient writings, twisting facts to suit their own ideas. Corrections, heralded by young thinkers, were censured by older men entrenched in positions of authority.

Nonetheless, a new Hellenism in medicine soon matched the classical revival in poetry, prose, painting, sculpture, architecture, and philosophy. Even in anatomy, re-examination led to progress. Andreas Vesalius (1514–1564) dissected human bodies and, comparing his results with those of Galen, found the Greek authority to be 50 percent incorrect. Galen, who lived in the

second century A.D., had published his research studies
in anatomy, and his books were used to teach medicine
for thirteen hundred years. In that many centuries, no
one had challenged his work, nor had anyone thought
to check facts of anatomical dissection against his claims.
Vesalius, as a result of his daring, was called a heretic
who should be burned at the stake. After study, his
dissensions were shown to be so accurate that many
scholars and students rallied to his defense, and die-
hards were forced to admit the new anatomy of Vesalius
into medical teaching programs.

New medical terms became so abundant that physicians and research experts discussed the need for a professional dictionary. One of the first was compiled by Sym-
phorien Champier of Lyons, France, whose student
days were spent in Italy. As has been stated, dissemi-
nation of new medical knowledge was accelerated by
the discovery of movable type for printing books, but
then, as today, no doctor or medical investigator could
know or keep up with the flood of published scientific
papers. In 1545, Konrad von Gesner published his
Bibliotheca universalis, a compilation of every known
thesis, dissertation, and book on many medical matters.
Physicians avidly sought copies.

The rebirth of art, philosophy, and religion gave
hope to people of all classes. The new medicine made
it possible to succor or cure the ill, who were treated
by physicians with ever increasing information. The
Renaissance revival of learning created a vital atmo-

sphere for another giant step forward in the history of medicine, making it possible for doctors to open new areas that eventually led to the saving of lives by the millions.

Four hundred years elapsed between the sixteenth-century Age of Learning and the twentieth-century Age of Space, but the threads of daring investigation and humanistic purpose tie the two periods together.

In our book *Scientists Who Changed the World,** we examined the lives, influence, and dedication of men of science whose ideas were so revolutionary, so volcanic, that the world was never again the same after they lived. Among them were the giants of medicine: Hippocrates, Galen, Vesalius, Harvey, Morton, Lister, Jenner, Pasteur, and Freud.

In this book, we concentrate on the times, lives, and contributions of other medical men. Their daring ideas, creative investigations, dramatic discoveries, and, above all, their adherence to the basic humanism established in the sixteenth century aided their fellow men of future generations in saving lives of numberless patients.

It is not possible to name every doctor or research specialist who contributed to the skein of medical knowledge. With the aid of medical scholars and historians, we have selected a few men whose works clearly illustrate how and why the future always depends on the past. To be named the originator of a lasting move-

* Dodd, Mead & Company, New York, 1960.

ment is a distinction accorded only to persons of unusual stature. Those whose lives and works are highlighted here are such men, men who saved lives by their creative heresy.

Fracastoro, wealthy and cultivated, gave the first accurate description of typhus and syphilis, and fathered epidemiology. Paracelsus, poor and boorish, pioneered the modern theory of chemical treatment of diseases.

Girolamo Fracastoro

1483*–1553, *Italian*

Paracelsus

1493–1541, *Swiss-German*

Verona, elegant jewel of a town situated seventy miles inland from Venice, was the ideal setting for a leader of the Italian Renaissance. The village—cool in summer, warm in winter—was surrounded with vast acres of farmland. Vineyards dripped with morning dew as peasants harvested the grape crop. Wheatfields were golden in August when workmen cut the grain with rhythmic sweeps of scythes. Songs of birds, laughter of people, and the clatter made by builders were the only sounds to break the stillness.

Outside the town, the wealthy landowner Girolamo Fracastoro led a life of luxury. A philosopher and phy-

* Birth date sometimes given as 1478.

sician, he spent his time delving into newly discovered facts and recently expounded ideas. He was a short, wide-shouldered man with a pinched nose, piercing eyes, and coal-black hair. Everyone in the area knew him. His was a familiar figure as, striding down the road to tend a patient, he read a book written in either Latin or Greek.

Content to live in the country, he was visited frequently by friends from the nearby University of Padua where he had studied medicine. He and his guests sang, discussed heretical ideas, and composed poetry in the meters of ancient Greece and Rome. Copernicus had been a fellow student at Padua, and many who visited Fracastoro at Verona were later to win equal fame.

Italy was an important center of the new era and, for a time, the University of Padua produced outstanding heretical thinkers. The town of Padua, then as now, tree-lined and somnolent, was a magnet for students and scholars from all over Europe. Youths from France, Germany, Spain, Portugal, and England learned from middle-aged men who had long pondered about and doubted the existing dogmas of religion, art, philosophy, medicine, and other sciences. The students, in turn, became innovators and new leaders. The amount of heretical suggestions, applications, and confirmations of new thought issuing from Padua was stupendous; in detail, the results of the revolutionary thinking there fill volumes on today's bookshelves. Men there envisioned the future, although they did not necessarily prove facts nor follow them to fulfillment of application.

Trained in that atmosphere, Fracastoro was a true humanist of the Renaissance, a man interested in many subjects. He was one of those who thought that an understanding of geography depended on a knowledge of astronomy; an understanding of medicine, on chemistry. "All things are related in some way, one to the other," he said. "To gain understanding, we must learn many subjects and find the point where each crosses the other." By day, he read newly printed books and old manuscripts; on cool, clear nights he watched the stars, seeking to corroborate what he had read. With astrolabe, compass, and globe, he followed reports of voyages to foreign countries. His wealth made it possible for him to entertain lavishly, and his guests were often explorers whom he plied with food and questions about far places.

While still quite young, Fracastoro had written a treatise on astronomy, contributed articles to journals of geography, prepared reports on his medical research to be read at the University of Padua, and lectured there to medical students.

As time passed, he became most interested in the prevalence of diseases that broke out in a single place, killing vast numbers of the population. He followed the spread of those diseases, asking theoretical questions. He read about the Black Death, a bubonic plague that had wiped out almost one-quarter of the population of

Europe and one-half of the population of England. Why had that dread disease hit so many people and in so many places at the same time? He knew that there had to be a reason beyond his knowledge, some specific physical cause.

Fracastoro investigated the spread of leprosy, typhus, tuberculosis, scabies, anthrax, and erysipelas. These followed a pattern, sweeping through one community but not spreading to another only twenty miles away. Why did some scourges decimate a single population yet not spread like pestilence? And what caused them to infect large numbers of people while certain illnesses affected only a few individuals?

While Fracastoro struggled to find reasons for the spread of known diseases, another, new to Europe, attacked large numbers of people. It infected rich and poor alike, kings and peasants, sailors and farmers. Fracastoro, examining patients, found that the symptoms were identical in every case. The victim first complained of pains in muscles and joints, then developed running, festering sores all over the body. Gradually the patient, wracked with excruciating pain, grew weak. Many died, and some patients, at last went mad.

The disease became widespread after King Charles VIII of France waged a campaign against the city of Naples in the late fifteenth century. Scores of his soldiers contracted the disease. Doctors who examined the soldier-patients exchanged reports with physicians in other sections of Europe where the disease had broken out. Fracastoro had read those reports before he studied cases in his own area. He knew that the medical profession had concluded that men contracted the disease after sexual intercourse with women who suffered from it. The women were carriers. Conversely, healthy women having intercourse with afflicted men then came down with the disease. Like the plague, tuberculosis, typhus, and similar diseases, the illness apparently was passed from one person to others by contact. The new disease was called the "love pestilence" because it appeared after sexual relations between a man and a woman.

Fracastoro did not lack for cases to study because a frightening proportion of the population suffered from it. With no experience to guide him, he experimented with first one treatment and then another. Finally, he observed that a compound of mercury at least slowed down the course of the disease, providing relief for the patient. It was relatively easy for Fracastoro to find victims in the early stages of the disease; in his day, sexual relations outside of marriage were commonly accepted and seldom stigmatized, then only lightly. When he found a man or a woman who had just contracted "love pestilence," he used his compound of mercury, occasionally effecting a cure before the case became virulent.

Year after year, he investigated the cause, course, and methods of curing "love pestilence," which was still on the increase. Finally, satisfied that he knew everything possible about the disease, he began to write a treatise on the subject. Being a cultivated man with the ability to write in the poetic, classical phrases of his day, he recorded his findings in poetic form instead of in the dry, factual, style of medical prose.

Today, no investigator would think of recording the results of his medical research in poetry, and few moderns would even have the ability to do so. To Fracastoro, it was logical that he should compose his findings in classical terms, especially since Apollo, god of poetry, was also the god of healing. For his story line, Fracastoro chose the tale of a shepherd boy, born on Mt. Sipylus, second son of the demigoddess Niobe. Changing the name of the mythical character to Syphilus, Fracastoro told how the young shepherd had sinned against the gods. In vengeance, they punished him with a disease called the "love pestilence." Syphilus, unrepentant, continued to have constant intercourse with women who, in turn, had sexual relations with other men. Syphilus infected the women, and they passed the disease on until, at last, the entire population was victimized by the disease.

Fracastoro's poetic treatise on the disease was published in three books in 1530; its title, *Syphilis Sive Morbus Gallicus.* In the trilogy, Fracastoro poetically described how the disease was passed from one person to another and the pathological progression from weakness through pustulation to death. In lyric form, he

also described detailed treatment prescribed by himself and by many other physicians. This was, in effect,
a textbook on the "love pestilence" that he called
syphilis, the name for the disease that is used today.

Fracastoro's poem was well-received, not only by
physicians but by all educated men of his day who fully
realized what a literary feat he had performed. Unfortunately, all too many of those who read the poem
were themselves suffering from syphilis. Happily, doctors throughout Europe learned from the trilogy on
syphilis how to alleviate the suffering of their patients
and even, in many cases, to effect a cure.

The Veronese scholar and physician continued to
study syphilis, reasoning that it was not unique, but
bore some relationship to other diseases that attacked
men. After reading in the rapidly expanding medical
literature of the time and correlating what he read with
his own research, he published another trilogy. This
one, in lucid prose, was *De Contagione,* published in
1546; it contained Fracastoro's theory of infectious and
contagious diseases. In a simple and direct style, he
propounded the theory that plagues striking down
large numbers of people in specific geographic areas
were transmitted from one to the other by an infectious
material. The material, he wrote, was often passed
directly by personal contact but could be transmitted
by way of an object handled by two persons, the infected and the healthy. He stated, in addition, that a
contagion was definitely known to be transmitted

through the air; the infectious material expelled into the air by a sick person floated around until it entered the body of another person, who became ill with the original disease.

Fracastoro pointed out that the "infectious material is not dead; it is, instead, something that lives and infects human beings and animals." Here, he was postulating the modern theory of bacteria, the minute organisms distributed in all matter, living and dead. Infectious diseases are so well understood today that what Fracastoro propounded sounds elementary; in his own time, it was revolutionary. He had never heard of or seen bacteria. The word was not then coined. The microscope was yet to be invented. He reasoned out his theory and to the best of his ability, with such equipment as was available, he substantiated and defended it.

Even if Fracastoro had ceased to do research at that point, fame and acclaim would have been his. But he continued to work, demonstrating that the fevers which strike men down each have a distinctive character. He separated them and gave detailed descriptions of each, pointing out how one differed from the others. Fracastoro is recognized as the first medical researcher to study typhus scientifically, and to use therapy for it that saved lives.

He always worked quietly and concentratedly in the Veronese countryside near Padua. Remaining aloof from the squabbles between advanced thinkers and those who conventionally held the line, he refused to be drawn into the conflicts that swirled about in the scholarly world.

In direct contrast, his contemporary Paracelsus took delight in open fights with conservatives and reactionaries, needling his adversaries and goading them into bitter conflict. He is known to have burned all of his own copies of the anatomical textbooks of Galen. This he did ostentatiously at night, surrounded by his followers, so "the flames of a dying dogma can be seen by the Pope in his chambers." Again unlike Fracastoro, Paracelsus was always on the go, traveling from one country to another, teaching here and there. He was a wandering medical investigator whose "dissection room is my mind and laboratory is the sick with whom I work and study."

Paracelsus was born Philippus Aureolus Theophrastus Bombastus von Hohenheim, at Einsiedeln, Switzerland, sometime in 1493. His father, a village physician, had the idea, then shared by few others, that character is formed in the first few years of a person's life. For that reason, the father taught his son to read and to write at an early age.

When the child, then called Theophrastus, was ten, his widowed father moved to the town of Villach. There a Count Füger, had established a school of mining with his profits from smelting plants. In this school, Theophrastus studied mining, metallurgy, and chemistry. He was fascinated particularly by the way natural elements repel and attract each other, and how they merge to form new substances. Soon, with learning beyond that of his schoolmates, he chose to study in Italy, enrolling at the University of Ferrara. After concentrating his efforts on Latin and Greek, he became expert at translations in the subtly beautiful style of the Renaissance. The youth even Latinized his name and was thereafter known as Paracelsus. It would be more in keeping with his character had he chosen one of his own real names—Bombastus! His teachers predicted for him a scholastic future in peaceful confines given over to humanistic studies. But true to his nature, Paracelsus revolted against the contemplative life when he recalled the physical suffering of miners and smelters and others who lacked adequate medical care.

He enrolled for medical studies but soon left the university. In later years he wrote, "If a man desires to become acquainted with many diseases, he is forced to depart on his travels. If he travels far, he will gain much experience and will acquire much knowledge." Paracelsus was an itinerant physician, living among peasants and workers of all kinds, caring for the ill, and studying their sicknesses.

While he wandered, he kept personal case records that he compared with those published in medical books. Gradually, his idea of nature as the supreme healer took shape. He published fragments of a somewhat fanciful, mystical book entitled *Paramirum,* in which he set down his ideas of natural healing. It was

ernments; in recognition of their stature and service, a crest and seal had been awarded to the proud Fabricii. Genes of their greatness were the patrimony of the family heir.

Teachers of the young and amiable Fabricius were impressed by his keen mind and by his amazing memory. In his seventeenth year, he registered at the University of Padua and became the protégé of the Italian noble Lippomano. Fabricius lived in the nobleman's house, studying logic, philosophy, Latin, and Greek at the university. Those subjects, however, were not his forte. Medicine was his chief interest, and a career in it, his goal. At the University, he progressed so impressively that he was chosen to assist Fallopius, the man who first described female ovaries and the Fallopian tube, the oviduct that serves as the passageway for the eggs to the uterus.

Fabricius received his doctor of medicine degree when he had just passed his twentieth birthday. Continuing as assistant to Fallopius in his lectures on anatomy, Fabricius also accompanied the famous physician on his rounds visiting the sick. Fabricius required only a few hours of sleep and, being an omnivorous reader, had the time to combine the study of vast numbers of new books with that of practical medicine.

After the death of his mentor Fallopius in 1562, the chair of surgery at Padua remained vacant without any formal replacement being made until April 10, 1565 when Fabricius was appointed to the chair, receiving an annual salary of 100 florins. He lectured on various medical subjects and started his first public course in anatomy on December 18, 1566; it lasted for 22 days, including Christmas, and ended on January 5, 1567. His brilliant teaching and anatomical demonstrations added to Padua's fame, and he was reappointed to the chair of anatomy in October 1571, at double his original salary. With his salary doubled once more, he was reappointed for a second time six years later, and, for a third time, in 1584.

The state and university governing bodies, in recognition of the contributions of Fabricius, particularly his contributions to Padua's prestige, built a special building for his lecture-demonstrations of dissection of the human body. The windowless amphitheater of anatomy was constructed of wood with circular galleries, one atop the other. Spectators at Fabricius's demonstrations were arranged in RHIP (Rank Has Its Privileges) order. Fabricius sat at the dissecting table in a magnificent chair of carved wood. University officials sat on stools placed behind him. Seats located opposite Fabricius and the university officials, were occupied by Rectors of the city of Padua and visiting dignitaries from Venice. Other professors stood behind them. Students leaned over the rails of the circular galleries that rose from the pit; older students stood on the first tiers; younger ones were in the galleries above. Two candelabra, each holding three large candles, flanked the professor. Eight selected students, each holding one large candle, stood nearby.

When all was in readiness in the amphitheater, a trap door close to the dissecting table opened and a carefully prepared cadaver rose from the cellar beneath. In that dramatic atmosphere, with its positions jealously guarded by faculty and officials, all rank conscious, Fabricius lectured intermittently for nearly half a century. He often gave lectures out-of-doors and sometimes spoke informally at his home.

Throughout the forty-eight years that he served as professor at the University of Padua, Fabricius also was an active attending physician. He visited and cured the rich and the poor, the famous and the undistinguished. Records of his rich and famous patients have come down through history. In 1581, the Duke of Mantua called Fabricius to attend his brother, subsequently cured of a fever. Fabricius treated Galileo in the summer of 1606 and again in the fall of 1608, and had as a patient Carlo de Medici, son of Ferdinand I and Christina of Lorraine. When Paolo Sarpi, a noted philosopher and historian, was stabbed in a midnight assassination attempt in 1607, Fabricius and his pupil Adrianus Sipeglius were called to Venice. For the skill with which the wounded man was treated, Fabricius was made a Knight of St. Mark by vote of the Venetian senate.

His fame spread, and gentry of other lands sent messengers to consult with Fabricius. Even the tough, irascible Sigismund III of Poland sent his personal physician, Johannes Gallus, to Padua for consultation with Fabricius about the ruler's illness. The ministrations of Fabricius brought him not only fame but a great fortune in gold and gifts of treasure. From his emolument, he was able to live in a fabulous villa known as La Montagnola.

Families of his poor and ignorant patients kept no diaries noting his generosity in constant attention to charity cases. However, in various chronicles of the times there are numerous references to the popularity of Fabricius with the masses. The writings cite the numbers of lowly persons who paid homage to Fabricius and tell of the fruits, vegetables, flowers, and farm animals given to him by grateful patients who were country folk.

During his years of medical practice, Fabricius kept careful case records of his diagnosis, therapy, and its effectiveness with specific patients. He correlated his conclusions with his own scientific research. His anatomical work was so painstaking that he found the conclusions of Vesalius to be erroneous in numerous instances. Vesalius wrote that the lens of the eye was centered on the eyeball; Fabricius correctly described the lens as being near the forward rim. The writings of Vesalius were confused by circumlocution, and his wordiness led him astray from the subject so that he often failed to note certain salient details. From observations of dissected cadavers, Fabricius assembled anatomical facts that had been omitted by Vesalius.

According to the writings of Fabricius and of others who worked with him, he did not dissect cadavers simply to improve his skill. He was primarily interested in the comparative data by which he could correlate the functions and actions of interior parts of the body. This technique led him to the discovery of the valves in the veins, which he scientifically described for the first time. That simple statement expressed one of his greatest contributions to medical science. Modern cardiologists agree that his original demonstration of valves in veins was of utmost value to the development of cardiovascular knowledge.

A skilled surgeon, Fabricius often prolonged operations so that he might examine specific portions of the anatomy laid bare by his instruments. He was severely criticized for this practice, but it was the only way to examine internal organs that otherwise could not be seen. He meticulously recorded his observations and published his finding so that other surgeons might learn from his experience.

Choosing newly pregnant ewes, cows, and rabbits as experimental animals, Fabricius studied the reproductive system and revived the Aristotelian study of the growth of the *embryo*, the organism of life that exists during the first three months of pregnancy. He first examined three-week-old embryos, then others seven weeks old, and finally those that had reached the age of three months. His study of the embryo was his second outstanding contribution to medical science. He wrote extensively on embryonic development, tracing the embryo from initial pregnancy to development at three months.

During a lecture-demonstration on January 22, 1579, he dissected three cadavers, one of a woman who had died in labor six hours earlier. While the audience in the amphitheater watched the unfamiliar procedure, he minutely examined the reproductive system of the cadaver and gave his opinion on the cause of the woman's death. At another demonstration, he dissected the cadaver of a pregnant female, demonstrating to those present the formation of the woman's uterus and the substance of the placenta. Through his thorough investigation and explanations of the reproductive system, Fabricius became one of the outstanding authorities in the field now known as *gynecology*. Since all new facts he learned were published for the profession, his reports, widely circulated in Europe, were of great assistance to physicians and midwives who attended patients during pregnancy and at childbirth.

A favorite student of Fabricius's was William Harvey, a young Englishman, who wrote of his professor, "I wait with the greatest anticipation and excitement for each of his demonstrations." Returning home from Padua, Harvey received the patronage of Sir Lancelot Brown, physician to Her Majesty Queen Elizabeth the First. Later Harvey, as physician to King James I, was given permission to dissect specimens of the finest animals in the Royal Park.

Harvey's research was concentrated on the blood stream and the heart. He proved that the blood does not flow from liver to heart to brain in the circuitous system guessed at by Galen. Harvey, correctly charting the course of the blood, established conclusively that it circulates through the body. In one of his published papers, he stated unequivocally that this vital discovery might never have been made had it not been for the teaching of Fabricius.

As the years passed, Fabricius unwillingly was caught up in the petty squabbles and political bickering that shook the University of Padua. Ensnared, he was not always able to prove himself right in the controversies. A barb continually thrown at him was that he was not consistent in the preparation and presentation of his lecture-demonstrations. The charge obviously was well-founded. When one reads his life story, his letters, his professional papers, it becomes evident that Fabricius chafed under increased demands for ever more lecture-demonstrations. He was restive when forced to confine himself only to repeated lectures to large groups of students. His major interests were medical therapy and anatomical research.

Having long been placid and calm, Fabricius gradually became erratic in his teaching and quick to anger. The infighting of the faculty and the time he had to waste in answer to repeated warnings from the Rectors encroached on his hours for research. Disputes increased in number. The quarrels became bitter. A Sicilian colleague even drew a knife on Fabricius.

Unable to stand the pressure any longer, he resigned his position at Padua in November 1613, and retired to La Montagnola. At his villa, Fabricius continued his research and gathered around him students of high caliber for whom he had intellectual regard and personal affection. Always a prolific writer whose bibliography is extensive, he continued to commit his thoughts to paper.

From middle age on, Fabricius suffered from ill health, which bothered him more each successive year. A widower for many years, he was attended by a grandniece, Semidea, who was his adopted child. When she became engaged to a young medical student, Fabricius approved the marriage, which was performed in the private chapel of La Montagnola on May 9, 1619. Fabricius was seriously ill, but he appeared to be happy and enthusiastic at the ceremony. Without his beloved Semidea, Fabricius failed to recuperate from the illness that he brushed aside as unimportant at the time of the wedding festivities. He died on the evening of May 21, and he was buried beside his wife in the chapel of San Francesco in Padua.

In the funeral oration, Johannes Thuilius said, "One day, one hour, one little moment has taken from us what centuries will not restore. There has been removed from among us that man whose equals, to say nothing of superiors, in everyone's opinion it would be hard to find."

The Sicilian who only a few years earlier had drawn a knife against Fabricius wept bitter tears at his funeral.

Addison, diagnostician and teacher, made the classic description of pernicious anemia and wrote on the nature and the functions of the ductless glands.

Thomas Addison

1793–1860, *British*

"If Addison's father had not moved from Lanercost, in Cumberland, to Long Benton, near Newcastle-upon-Tyne, where Thomas was born, the boy may well have become one of the world's best known authorities on geology, geography or farming. So great were his powers of diagnosis, he would have reached the top in whatsoever area he chose to work. Fortunately, because countless people owe their lives to him, he chose the humane field of medical science."

Those words by a contemporary, John Whitmar, reflect the esteem in which Addison was held by his own colleagues and students as well as later generations of physicians.

Whitmar may have been correct in suggesting that but for chance and a family move the great diagnostician might have been a scientist of the land. His ancestors lived in the tiny town of Lanercost, in Cumberland, a county of northern England that borders the Irish Sea with Solway Firth to the west and Scotland to the north. The pastoral region, part of the Lake District of England, is a center of dairy farming, cattle grazing, and sheep raising; and of quarrying, mining, smelting, and textile industries. Lanercost was not, however, a prosperous community, and Addison's father much improved his economic condition by moving to Long Benton, where Thomas was born in April 1793. His father, after operating a grocery store, became a flour merchant, making more money than any Addison who ever lived at Lanercost.

The senior Addison's aspirations for his son to have advantages, particularly those of education, were realistic because of Thomas Addison's mental ability. The father, recognizing that his son was gifted, retained the local schoolmaster as part-time tutor in Latin for Thomas. He was prepared by his proud teacher for entrance examinations to the University of Edinburgh. At seventeen, Thomas was admitted to the university and traveled north to Edinburgh, the "Modern Athens," or the "Athens of the North." He arrived with sixteen textbooks, a few personal belongings, and a highly developed interest in medicine. In later years, he wrote,

> "I had already read in the Latin language more than one hundred epics of medicine. When I read of what had been learned by men in the past and thought about all

that was yet to be discovered, I burned with desire to follow the footsteps of those who offered balm to the ill."

At Edinburgh, Addison followed the conventional curriculum of the course in medicine but, also, because his professors were immediately impressed with his evident ability and obvious determination to succeed, they allowed him to go with them on their rounds visiting patients. The young student was invited to the homes of professors, too, and had the opportunity to hear them talk informally and to speak with them on matters beyond those included in scheduled lectures. John Whitmar reports that from early on Addison's dissection of cadavers was done "with the skill of an artist and the dedication of a cleric." Long after fellow-students had left the lecture hall, Addison plied his professors with provocative questions, and when others had left the dissecting room, Addison stayed on for a final and closer examination of the cadaver.

When Addison received his doctor of medicine degree on August 1, 1815, at the age of twenty-two, he was offered a wide choice of rich practices in several cities. However, instead of becoming the colleague of some fashionable doctor, he chose to accept a position as house surgeon at Lock Hospital in London. After making his decision, Addison wrote to a friend,

"I have three desires and three duties. One is to become a medical investigator. Another is to pass on medical knowledge to others. And, finally, I wish to care for the sick. In a great hospital or university I can combine all three, and thereby pay my debt to many who have helped me."

At Lock Hospital, Addison was an eager member of the house staff; even when off duty, he roamed the hospital finding work to do, day or night. In time, he was assigned to help Charles Bateman, a doctor at the Public Dispensary, that service being in addition to Addison's work in surgery. At the dispensary, he became interested in skin diseases. Later discourses and writings indicate the accuracy of his knowledge of a wide variety of diseases of the skin. Experts claim that Addison opened new paths of diagnosis and treatment that were invaluable to the advance of the field of dermatology.

After five years as a novitiate and apprentice, "I was given one of the greatest gifts any medical investigator could wish," Addison wrote. "I became a pupil of Guy's Hospital." Even then, that London hospital had achieved international recognition for its famous men of medicine and the medical discoveries that had been made there, one more outstanding than the other. Although known for its atmosphere of medical innovation, Guy's was also famed for its patient care. The hospital's reputation as one of the world's greater medical centers prevails to the present day.

True to the statement he made on going to Lock Hospital, Addison combined diagnostic studies with

research and therapy. References to him as a great diagnostician are found in the archives of the College of
Physicians in London. One source reports that, at a
moment's notice, Addison could quote the apt portion
of works by earlier diagnosticians from Hippocrates to
Helmuth. "His precursors were his stimuli; his own
powers of observation were his genius."

Addison raised the art of diagnosis to new heights,
and the most cogent tribute to him as diagnostician is
contained in a eulogy recorded by the College of Physicians. "Possessing unusually vigorous perceptive
powers, being shrewd and sagacious beyond the average
man, the patient before him was scanned with a pen-
etrating glance from which few diseases could escape
detection. He never reasoned from half-discovered
facts, but would remain at the bedside with a dogged
determination to track out the disease to its very source
for a period which ofen wearied his class and his attendant friends. To those who knew him best, his power
of searching into the complex framework of the body
and dragging the hidden malady to light appeared un-
rivalled."

His "perceptive powers" were early concentrated on
a single area of pathology—the lungs. Addison, the
determined diagnostician, began a longtime study of
normal lungs, pneumonia, pneumonic phthisis, and
phthisis in general. Phthisis stems from the classical
Greek word meaning to waste away, and Greek physicians applied it to any disease involving the wasting

away or the deterioration of tissue. Phthisis, narrowed in meaning, today commonly refers to consumption.

Addison studied the pathology of the disease of the lungs that we know as consumption, or tuberculosis, a word first used in 1810. The disease itself is ancient, as old as the history of civilization. The Babylonians referred to it; Hippocrates called it consumption; Galen, in the second century B.C., mentioned the possibility that the disease was transmitted from one person to another. In 1689, Richard Morton, a British physician, published a treatise in which he discussed the disease and specifically noted the "wasting away of the body."

After research on cadavers and the treatment of living patients, Addison wrote many papers on the subject, giving his opinions of various aspects. With his "dogged determination to track out the disease," he studied old and new written records of it, observed its course at the bedside and in the laboratory. He did research in the field, visiting mines and smelting plants where the workers were attacked by phthisis. Addison lectured and wrote incisively about his studies and observations of the *tubers* that attacked the lungs, describing in detail the progress of the disease. Many of his contemporaries were certain that his research into and treatment of tuberculosis would be his greatest contributions to medicine. They underestimated the scope of his ability.

Addison was a well-known figure at Guy's. In middle

age, he was a large, solidly built man. His massive head was set powerfully on muscular shoulders. His facial features were strong and craggy, the nose large, the chin broad and stern; shaggy eyebrows and deep-set hazel eyes distinguished the face. Addison exuded vigor in physiognomy and manner. Normally mild, he became impassioned when lecturing or speaking face to face with anyone who would listen to his bursts of enthusiasm for his work in research and with patients.

Toward the end of his active years, Addison made a medical contribution that overshadows his work with tuberculosis. At least popularly, his fame depends on his study of ductless glands, particularly suprarenal glands.

Ductless glands and duct glands do not function alike. Duct glands, such as the sweat glands, discharge the products of their activity into the body by means of ducts or tubes that allow the free flow of the products. Ductless glands release their products directly into the blood stream. Glands that are ductless include the hypothalamic, pituitary, thyroid, parathyroids, adrenals, thymus, testes, ovaries, part of the pancreas, and possibly the pineal body. Ductless glands are part of the endocrine system of the body made up of organs characterized by their ability to produce those active chemical substances, the hormones. These are vital to proper functioning of the body.

The investigation of Addison was directed to the adrenal glands, which are located above each kidney. The word adrenal comes from the Latin: *ad*—near, toward, by, above; and *renalis*—of or belonging to the kidney. Each normal adrenal gland, although it weighs only about three grams, performs vital functions. The inner portion of the gland, called the *medulla,* manufactures adrenalin. The outer layer of the gland is the cortex, which produces about twenty-nine varieties of hormone, some with several types of activity, some with only one type of activity. A hormone is a substance that excites action, goes to one or more portions of the body, and, upon reaching its destination, stimulates an action needed for the normal functioning of the body.

Addison was aware that many human beings are unfortunate heirs to a certain disease with specific symptoms: The patient, whose skin turns to a yellow-bronze color, is subject to anemia, diarrhea, low blood pressure, weight loss, and upsets of the gastrointestinal system. The body is dehydrated, and the patient becomes mentally and physically fatigued. Addison first sought for the anatomical basis of certain changes in skin color and found it by correlating the symptoms of the living with the anatomical changes observed during autopsies of deceased persons. Aided by chemical analysis and scientific observation, Addison concluded that the debilitating disease was caused by the malfunctioning of the adrenal glands, located directly above the kidney. This renal failure was called *Addison's anemia*—often miscalled pernicious anemia. Addison's anemia is *not* pernicious anemia.

In 1855, Addison published a brief, but masterly and lucid, description of the disease entitled *On the Constitutional and Local Effects of Disease of the Suprarenal Capsules,* that is, disease of the glands above the kidneys. His description of cause, condition, progress, and final phase of a specific disease was so accurate, so complete, that it ever since has been called "Addison's disease." Many endocrinologists, specialists in the pathology of endocrine glands, credit Addison with important contributions to their field. They say that without his vital research the science of endocrinology might well be a century behind its present state, and millions of human beings who are alive today might have died.

Guy's Hospital was imbued with Addison's spirit of investigation, of dedication to practice and teaching. He was a major force in helping to sustain the hospital's world-wide renown. Addison retired, and died at Brighton in 1860. He is buried in the chapel at Lanercost, Cumberland, the region where his forefathers lived.

The controversy about which of his contributions was the greatest continued after his death:

"To those who knew Addison it is almost absurd to rest his fame on a discovery made towards the close of his career and when his clinic teaching had reached its end. To pupils his essay *Supra Renal Diseases* is nothing compared with what he did during his long series of years in the elucidation of the forms of phthisis and other diseases . . . his work on *Supra Renal Diseases* is a trifle; to the outside world and to posterity it may be that which will perpetuate his fame. Yet to us, the greatness of Addison is as a man of science who cares and cares deeply, who delves to the bottom of each symptom, who has the powers of explanation, who trained others to believe they would be great."

When so much that Addison contributed to the field of medicine was of such merit, it seems otiose for the controversy about degrees of importance to exist. Would that every man could engender the same devotion and could contribute so much to humanity. Addison, at once famous and humble, was a humanist typical of the earlier Renaissance tradition.

Louis, recognized as a medical investigator and physician, established the science of statistics and applied it to the study of human diseases.

Pierre Charles Alexandre Louis

1787–1872, *French*

Electronic computers are a twentieth-century invention, affecting practically every part of daily life. Whirring out facts and figures, miscellaneous and specific information, the computers aid business, industry, government agencies, and the sciences. People in this mechanistic age accept them as essential to the various institutions where they are installed and tolerate, as an unavoidable part of living, the coded marks or punched holes on computer cards. It is difficult for those with this point of view to realize that the science of statistics, crucial to computers, is relatively new, and that it was scoffed at in the time of its original presentation. The French doctor, Pierre Louis, who in 1828 published an article on the statistical approach to medicine provoked nothing but laughter from his Parisian colleagues.

Pierre Louis was born during troubled times in France and matured in an age of turmoil, not only in politics but in his chosen profession, medicine. His birthplace was the tiny town of Ai on the Marne River, where his father owned a vineyard.

Pierre was only two years old when the Parisian mob marched on Versailles in the fall of 1789, signaling the start of the French Revolution; he was eight years old when the boy-king Louis XVII disappeared. The young country boy paid scant attention to the turbulent events of rising and falling governments, the Directory, the failure of the First Republic, and the quixotic, disastrous rule of Napoleon Bonaparte. Pierre, quick in his studies, determined to secure a university education, although his family lacked funds for taxes or even for the necessities of daily sustenance. Disregarding the events of the larger world, he worked at menial jobs until he saved enough money to venture to Paris to start law studies. After a few months he shifted from law to medicine and won his doctor's degree in 1813, just one year before Napoleon abdicated and was banished to Elba.

Degree in hand, Louis was faced with a major decision. Should he stay in France to practice, or should he accept an offer to go to Russia as personal physician to the family of the Count of Saint-Priest? A serious consideration of medicine as it was practiced in France

settled the matter for Louis. François Joseph Victor
Broussais was the most influential doctor in France,
serving as dictator and examplar to all others. Like him,
they treated patients roughly, no matter what their
ailment. The methods for healing regularly produced
vomiting, purging, and sweating whether those violent
measures were necessary or not. Bleeding patients
with leeches was common practice, and it was reported
that more than thirty-three million leeches were im-
ported to France in a single year. Faced with the prospect of practicing medicine in an environment so un-
sympathetic to him, Pierre Louis set out for Russia.

He served the family of the Count of Saint-Priest for
a few years and then traveled from town to town in
Russia, finally stopping in 1820 at Odessa where a
virulent epidemic of diphtheria was raging. Always
sensitive to human suffering, he was dispirited by his
inability to ease the patients struck down by diphtheria
or to prevent the deaths of victims of the fever. In a
letter to a friend, he described himself as emotionally
upset by the realization of how little he knew about
epidemics, and said that he was thinking of a return
to Paris where "certainly physicians have discovered
means by which to control mass outbreaks of contagious disease."

Louis did return to Paris and was immediately dis-
illusioned. French doctors, still bleeding patients with
leeches as a cure-all, knew little about epidemics. Reading, listening, and questioning, Louis searched in vain

for just one doctor who was a dependable investigator. Finding no man who could help him in his search for answers to many pressing medical questions, he set about to find out for himself those things that he wanted to know. As a member of the staff of the Charity Hospital, he supervised work in two large wards and was able to spend long hours in the autopsy room, examining the bodies of patients who had died.

He rarely left the hospital, leading a celibate, monastic life centered on research and therapy. Like so many other outstanding men who made medical history, he kept detailed records of every patient he treated. Like Addison, practicing across the English Channel, Louis was concerned about the prevalence of phthisis and studied all of its manifestations and phases. In 1825, he published a book on phthisis, basing it on a correlation of works he had read on the wasting-away diseases with his own records of patients from his wards and examinations of cadavers.

Louis kept his meticulous records for a specific reason: he needed them to test a theory that slowly had been developing in his mind. He thought that by correlation of innumerable facts concerning symptoms, progress, cure, or loss of patients it would be possible to predict with reasonable accuracy the statistical probability of how a diagnosed case would go. Convinced that he was thinking along sound lines, he left Paris and settled in a cell-like room at Brussels. There, he worked night and day on case histories, comparing and rechecking data, studying and examining facts, filing and cross-filing records. After months of concentrated work, Louis put together a statistical report on every facet of many diseases; it was his hope that his report would aid other doctors in diagnosis, prognosis, and therapy.

At that period, the early nineteenth century, immediate diagnosis of a disease was rare, and it was impossible for a doctor either to predict the course the disease would take or to prescribe treatment on any but a trial-and-error basis. Louis was aware that no two cases of even the same disease are exactly alike, but he was convinced that guidelines could be made available to physicians. Those guidelines, he reasoned, could and had to be arrived at by statistical study. Looking over the statistics he had assembled from the accurate records made for many patients, he began to see exactly how his statistical approach to medicine would work.

If, for example, his figures showed that one group of people with a certain disease all died after a planned course of therapy and another group with the same disease but slightly different symptoms were cured by the same treatment, an attending doctor could use the statistical records to guide him in the care of patients with that disease. Any doctor aware of the facts in Louis's statistical studies could make a diagnosis, scientifically arrive at a prognosis, and prescribe a treatment.

There was a serious drawback to these well-laid

plans; lazy doctors, too indolent to search records for facts, laughed at the statistical report published in Paris in 1828. Many doctors did take the time to examine the statistical method, but few attempted to adopt it. Louis was attacked on the grounds of too limited a sampling of patients; medical men said that statistics garnered from relatively few patients were fallible and not to be trusted. Louis, answering his critics, admitted the limitation of his system but stated that a day would come when a law of averages would be propounded, and then accurate statistics could be developed.

After Louis married, he took up private practice, becoming a leader in the medical circles of France but never losing either his faith or interest in statistical methods. He continued to make new contributions to the diagnosis and therapy of tuberculosis, asthma, and related respiratory diseases. He was the first man to distinguish between typhoid fever and typhus. Investigating the former, he attempted to determine whether those born and raised in Paris were more susceptible to the disease than those born in the country who had recently moved to Paris. Basing his study on statistical data, he concluded that native-born Parisians were more susceptible to typhoid than country-bred people residing in the city.

A number of medical investigators, convinced of the merits of Louis's statistical approach, formed the Society

of Medical Observations in Geneva, Switzerland, in
1832. The Society expanded from its original membership to include doctors from England, Ireland, France,
Germany, the United States, and Australia. Members
fed statistics to the Geneva headquarters, attended
meetings, and agreed to medical practices dependent
on the direction set by statistical evidence. Scholarly
papers published by the organization were distributed
throughout the world. The Society terminated its activities in 1837, but during its existence some of the
finest mathematical minds of the time contributed to
the development of the *méthode numérique,* making
additions, deletions, and corrections to Louis's basic
method. Cross-indexed volumes, printed in seven lan-
guages, immediately aided physicians and eventually
stimulated young mathematicians to develop a science
of statistics as applied to medicine.

In 1861, Louis again was the object of derision when
he predicted that someday someone with a mind more
mechanical than his would invent a machine to aid the
statistician in his work. The laughter of his detractors
would have had a hollow ring could they have foreseen
the efficiency of the numerous inventions that help
statisticians today.

The *méthode numérique* is commmplace in our lives
today. It is basic to the methodology in schools of medicine, hygiene, and public health, to the procedures of
government agencies and industrial organizations. Few
of the millions of people whose lives are touched by the

results of the work of Pierre Louis even know his name, much less the fact that he alone created, impelled, and established the science of statistics. In our contemporary world it has gone far beyond medicine into every realm of human activity.

Sims, *founder of modern operative gynecology, in-vented diagnostic and surgical instruments and developed an operation that still is performed.*

James Marion Sims

1813–1883, *American*

Fame made it possible for James Marion Sims to indulge the urge for travel that he developed at a very early age. Restless and energetic, he was carried away with several enthusiasms before he settled on medicine. In medical practice, he moved from place to place when the wanderlust became too much for him. As a doctor of established reputation, he traveled widely in the United States and in foreign countries in answer to invitations from medical societies and hospital staffs.

Sims was born on January 25, 1813, in a village that was hardly a spot on the map of Lancaster County, South Carolina. When he showed signs of being precocious, his parents began to argue about his future. They were in agreement only in wanting for him a social and professional status higher than any member of the family had yet been able to achieve. The mother wanted her son to be a Presbyterian minister and, eventually, a bishop of the Church. The father wanted the boy to study for the law in the hope that he might one day be a judge. James, caught in the his parents' cross fire, was enthusiastic about neither the ministry nor the law.

He vacillated in his own ambitions, deciding at one time that he might be a banker, and again a farmer, and, at still another time, an ornithologist. By the time he graduated with honors from South Carolina College in 1832, he had settled on medicine for his career.

With no funds for medical-school tuition, Sims stayed in his home town as medical apprentice to an elderly physician, Dr. Churchill Jones. Sims wrote in his autobiography that Jones practiced medicine with the minimum of medical knowledge and the maximum of intuition based on long experience. Sims read what few books Jones owned, and he accompanied the older doctor on his rounds and observed how he treated patients. Within his limited sphere, Jones apparently did the best he could for his patients and, for one with so little formal training, was amazingly skillful at surgery. He had an innate sensitivity for operative procedures and effected his best cures through surgery. The elder doctor, highly respected by all, inspired young Sims to choose surgery as his own special field.

Leaving Jones, he enrolled in Jefferson Medical College, Philadelphia, and in his second year was made assistant in surgery to Dr. George McClellan. Sims, an excellent student, was endowed with abundant imagination and natural curiosity, both attributes approved by McClellan, who also recognized Sims's obvious ability as a surgeon. At that time, anesthesia was not yet in use, and McClellan, although often erratic and impatient, was compassionate for his patients who, while conscious, underwent surgery. As McClellan operated, he chatted with the patient, assuring him that the ordeal would soon be over and attempting to cheer him with the prospect of being well and happy. Sims quickly picked up McClellan's bedside manner and profited from the operating-room experience.

At that time, however, actual courses in anatomy at Jefferson were sketchily presented and students were not permitted to dissect cadavers. Sims not only felt a lack in his training, which ended in 1835, but he also realized that to be a good surgeon he would have to know more about the human anatomy. He signed up for a course, *Regional Anatomy and Surgical Anatomy*, taught privately by a Philadelphia surgeon and, on its completion of that course, returned to South Carolina to practice in his own home town.

Sims had qualms and fears when he first entered medical practice, and with good reason. His first two patients were babies under two years of age. Even after thoroughly examining the infants, Sims was unable to diagnose their diseases. He had no idea what was wrong with either child. Both died. This inauspicious begin-

Girolamo Fracastoro

Paracelsus

Hieronymus Fabricius
ab Aquapendente

Thomas Addison

Pierre Charles
Alexandre Louis

James Marion Sims

Rudolf Virchow

Emil Theodor Kocher

David Ferrier

Paul Ehrlich

John Jacob Abel

Alexis Carrel

Frederick Grant Banting

Alexander Fleming

Howard Walter Florey

Ernst Boris Chain

ning did not long discourage Sims, who continued to examine patients, learning as his experience increased.

Driven by his impulse for a change of scene, Sims left his home town to set up practice in Montgomery, Alabama, soon leaving there for Mt. Meigs in the same state. Wherever he went, he quickly built up a profitable practice because of his sound reputation as surgeon. Patients knew him as a man who carefully studied every case, and then daringly attempted to correct the disorder.

Sims had interests in such disparate medical problems as clubfeet and strabismus, an eye disorder in which the optic axes cannot be directed to the same object. He studied the anatomy of the eye and cases of strabismus, trying several methods of surgical correction. None succeeded, but Sims wrote several papers on the subject that were read by the German doctor Friederich W. E. A. von Graefe, who ultimately devised the surgical technique for solving the optical correction of strabismus. When, years later, Sims met Graefe in Germany, the latter expressed his appreciation for the American's pioneering work with the eye defect.

The taunting endured by individuals with clubfeet distressed Sims, who hoped to find a way to spare people the indignity of being mercilessly persecuted for a physical deformity. A clubfoot is caused by a misplacement of the tendons of the foot, which makes the foot turn at an awkward angle. Sims studied the tendons, which are specialized extensions of muscle that anchor muscles to bone by means of connective tissue fibers that enter the bone structure. After he fully understood their function, he worked out a series of foot operations and devised special casts for the feet. His operations on clubfeet were not always totally successful, but he added knowledge to orthopedics, then a fairly new medical specialty.

Many of Sims's patients were women, both rich and poor. They had great faith in him as a healer of diseases contracted by women, especially those affecting the female reproductive system. Examination of the vagina of women patients up to that time had been difficult, and Sims invented a special instrument for the purpose. It was a duckbill speculum with which to dilate the vagina for internal examination. The instrument, still in use today, is known as Sims's speculum. The position for a gynecological examination that Sims invented is still a standard procedure. This special placement of his female patients on the examining table was devised in order to take full advantage of the view made possible by the duckbill vaginal speculum.

As the number of women patients increased, Sims saw more and more cases of *vesicovaginal fistula,* a fairly common condition. In this disease, a fistula, an abnormal opening, creates a channel through which urine leaks from the bladder directly into the vagina. The patient is incontinent, having no control over the flow of urine from the bladder to the outside of the body. The condition occurs from any number of causes, including childbirth.

Sims continually treated cases in which the problem was so far developed that women were bedridden, lying in sheets saturated with their own urine. Prolonged uncontrolled urination produced a festering of the vagina, an inflammation of its external parts, and an odor that sickened anyone who came near to the patient. Sims wrote, "Death would have been preferable. But patients of this kind never die from the disease; they must live and suffer their loathsome, disgusting plight." He often encountered victims of the disease who also had an opening that extended into the rectum that continually passed off involuntary intestinal gas.

In 1845, Sims first attempted surgical treatment of a woman suffering from vesicovaginal fistula. The operation failed, not only the first time, but again and again. His aim was to close the fistula in the bladder, but that was not easy to do because the opening through which urine escaped directly into the vagina sometimes was "no larger than a goose quill pen." Delicacy of surgical techniques was not then advanced; it was difficult to suture an opening. Sims tried one method of suture after another, failing to close the fistula time after time. His brother-in-law, Dr. Rush Jones, advised him to give up the surgical experiments. Women began to abandon Sims, preferring to lie in bed and suffer rather than undergo the doctor's examinations and crude surgery. Patients suffered excruciating pain during the operation until Sims learned to use the new anesthesia first proved effective in Boston.

After repeated failure, Sims had an idea. He would draw the suture knot tight and clamp it with forceps to make it more secure. Excitedly, he prepared a patient, performed the operation, and was pleased by the suture procedure, but again it failed him. The silk thread used for suturing did not hold a tight knot. It slipped. The bladder fistula reappeared, and the patient returned to her incontinent state.

While walking home from his office one day, Sims idly picked up a thin bit of brass wire. He recognized it as wire used in the latest kind of suspenders to make them more elastic. Passing the wire through his fingers, he noted how it stretched and then relaxed. That property gave him another idea. Taking the wire to a jeweler, Sims asked if one of the same size might be made of pure silver. The jeweler readily produced one. Sims again prepared a patient, pierced the torn parts of the bladder with four bits of silver wire, and passed them through tiny strips of lead placed on each side of the fistula. He tied the silver sutures, pressing the knots together with forceps. He had little hope for success, having been too often disappointed, but he passed a catheter, a small tube, into the vagina through the normal passage to the bladder in the expectation that urine would flow through the catheter, permitting the sutured bladder to remain flat and dry. The patient was a country woman named Anarcha, and the operation was the thirtieth that Sims had done on her. Uncertain as to the outcome of the silver-wire closing and the catheter treatment, Sims went home to await results.

The following morning he examined his patient, and to his great relief he found the "urine came from the bladder as clear and as limpid as spring water, and so it continued during all the time she wore the catheter." He waited a week, removed the silver sutures, and with the help of his duckbill speculum was able to observe the total lack of internal inflammation. The fistula was closed. That success came in 1849, four years after his first surgical attempt to close a vesicovaginal fistula.

In quick succession, Sims followed the same suture procedure with three other patients. Word of his successes spread quickly. Women came begging him to relieve them of their painful, odorous condition.

He wrote several medical papers on the successful operations and, after their publication, was invited to lecture at medical schools throughout the United States. In 1853, he went to New York to demonstrate his duckbill speculum, the Sims's position for gynecological examination, and the vesicovaginal-fistula operation. Doctors recommended Sims to their patients in need of surgery; patients themselves sought him out. He gathered a group of technical aides around him and, in a

temporary building in Manhattan set up a small clinic
called Woman's Hospital. The year was 1855. Two
years later, the hospital staff moved into newly built,
permanent quarters, and the Woman's Hospital received a charter from the State of New York.

On invitation, Sims demonstrated his operation in
England in 1861. Then he traveled to France, Germany, Italy, Spain, and Portugal. In answer to inquiries
from the Scandinavian countries, Belgium, Ireland,
Scotland, and Switzerland, Sims traveled far, driven by
a sense of duty and by his own indefatigable and energetic nature. The man who at the beginning of his
career had to escape from his home town and go on to
other communities to practice was a peripatetic teacher-
surgeon in Europe for eleven years. In 1872, he returned to his position as Surgeon-in-Chief at the
Woman's Hospital.

Honors were heaped on Sims. He heard himself
praised as the founder of modern operative gynecology.
The American Medical Association elected him president in 1876. His peers of the American Gynecological
Society made him their president in 1880. Just after his
seventieth birthday in 1883, he died, leaving behind
him a rich surgical heritage.

*Virchow dominated German medicine for fifty
years, established the cellular theory of diseases, and
influenced world-wide medical progress.*

Rudolf Virchow

1821–1902, *German*

Germany was in turmoil during the first half of
the nineteenth century. The effects of indecision and
change were obvious in its social structure and even in
the professions. Into a world of conflicts of ideology,
Rudolf Virchow was born and flourished as an active
liberal. With his complexities of personality and pro-
liferation of interests, Virchow might easily have made
his reputation in a field other than medicine. As it was,
during the time that he was making his outstanding
contributions in his chosen profession, he was also influential in politics and the arts. Dedicated to his work
and to causes he championed, he was guided by enthusiasms and hampered by bullheadedness. When
young, Virchow fought for those medical ideas that he
knew to be scientifically correct, and when old, he re-

sisted medical theories that had advanced beyond his own.

His stubborn nature served him well when, at a young age, he was in revolutionary opposition to the way of life followed by his domineering father, who was a martinet at home and a typical bureaucrat in the village of Schievelbein, Pomerania. There, Rudolf was born on October 13, 1821. The day was a Saturday, and it is recorded that the inconvenienced father was no end irritated by having to stay home from a hunting trip to await the birth of his child. The older Virchow, treasurer of Schievelbein, was disdainful of those who served under him in the small community, obsequious to those whom he served. He was a stern Prussian conservative and, in spite of political upheavals, remained so throughout his life. His son, even when quite young, was absorbed in the cause of the socialistic state.

After a youth that was unremarkable except for a persistent involvement in political progress and adherence to liberal ideals, he went to medical school in Berlin in 1839. He found himself in the mainstream of liberal thinking with no immediate need to combat those with whom he was associated. His patron was Johannes Müller, a leader of the German romantic movement that embraced the visual arts, music, literature, politics, and the sciences. In medicine, Müller actively opposed the cult of philosophical contemplation of nature. His own concept of basic science was well-founded, and he promoted the new theory of explaining nature through an experimental scientific approach.

Müller's influence on Virchow was immeasurable, and the two became fast friends. When Virchow was graduated from the Berlin Medical Faculty in 1843, he immediately was appointed to a responsible position at Berlin's Charité Hospital. He was never in any doubt as to the orientation of his research. When he was twenty-six, he and several friends began to publish a medical journal and in its first issue he defined his credo. He stated in part:

"The standpoint we aim to propound and which is now evident in this first issue is simply that of natural science. Practical medicine as applied to theoretical medicine and theoretical medicine as an intrinsic part of pathological physiology are ideals toward which we shall work, so far as they lie within the areas of our power."

He predicted that a new theory of the practice of medicine would emerge from a more precise study of the diseased anatomy and from application of clinical therapy. With Müller and other colleagues, Virchow urged that the medical profession bring to an end its philosophizing about the pathology of the body; they wanted facts about pathological anatomy to be scrutinized through scientific examination in the laboratory.

Virchow's triumphs in medicine resulted from happy circumstances. He had been born in the right era for his successes to be realized; he conceived the idea that made it possible for his method to work. The direct scientific approach to medicine was feasible because of new instruments available to Virchow and the recent discoveries of the cellular structure of vegetable matter on which his theories could be based and proven.

Prior to Virchow's meteoric appearance on the medical scene of Berlin, Müller's assistants had announced that the physiology of animals was based on the existence of an unknown number of cells. While there were some scientists who scoffed at that theory as preposterous, it already had been proved to the satisfaction of many scientists that vegetable matter was constructed of a system of related cells.

Scientists sought the answer to a key question: What are cells? Virchow brushed aside those answers arrived at only through philosophical rumination. He used direct scientific methods to study any problem and encouraged others to explore in their laboratories with microscopes and other research instruments. He arrogantly offered proof that cells grow from other cells, refuting different theories and quarreling violently with dissenting colleagues. Claiming that life is sustained only by a legitimate succession of cell formations, Virchow's battle cry was *"Omnis cellula e cellula!"*

Virchow's enthusiasm and energy, cyclonic in effect, were directed with unerring accuracy at a vortex of multiple medical problems. He relentlessly drove his technicians and medical assistants, but he asked no more of them than he demanded of himself. He continuously fought with those who continued to philosophize about pathological problems and lashed out at any who failed to substantiate theories with logical scientific investigations based on the cellular theory of pathology.

Adherents of Virchow's theory feverishly worked in their laboratories to get results that would support it. In his own laboratory, Virchow arrived at important discoveries. He meticulously investigated the pathology of *phlebitis,* a disease of human veins, and the blood itself, work that led directly to the isolation of *leukemia,* a disease of the blood, and to a description of the arterial pathology by which embolism and thrombosis occur in the blood vessels. Not content, as many men would have been, with his early discoveries, Virchow continued throughout his life to probe great numbers of pathological conditions; their listing would fill many pages if only the name of each disease and its description were given.

Virchow refuted the theory that thrombosis is the primary condition essential as the cause of phlebitis. He proved that phlebitis could occur in the blood vessel on a purely mechanical basis. Furthermore, he described and explained neuroglia; discovered both tyrosine and leucine in the human pancreas after death; investigated trichinosis; coined the name *arthritis deformans* for rheumatoid arthritis; introduced new terms such as *agennesia,* sterility, and *ochronosis,* a rare condition in which parts of the body are pigmented black. He also advanced medical knowledge of fungi which grow in the lungs.

While Virchow was engaged in multiple coordinated investigations, a plague erupted in Upper Silesia, the northern part of Prussia, later partitioned between Poland and Czechoslovakia. The rampant epidemic was popularly called famine fever, relapsing fever, and hunger typhus. The national government paid no attention to the plight of the stricken people until press and public clamored for action. In 1848, Virchow headed a medical team that went there to study the plague and to find a way to stop it as soon as possible.

Virchow at once recognized that the physical plague resulted from social problems. Europe was well into the Industrial Revolution and the weavers of Upper Silesia were victims of the movement. They were dependent for their income on dishonest entrepreneurs who made great profit from work farmed out to the weavers. Landowners of large estates also were crushing the cottage-industry personnel, masses of whom lived in misery. The diet of the people consisted of rotten food in small amounts. The air breathed was putrid because of unsanitary living conditions. Water was polluted. Miserable humans by the hundreds contracted typhus, a physical ailment resulting from adverse social conditions.

Virchow, ever one to oppose tyranny by the few and to champion the masses in distress, wrote and published a searing report that attacked landholders in general and the central national government in particular. In his report he flatly stated that the medical, mental, and material problems sapping the energy of the masses could only be solved by sweeping social reform, by a socialistic state where all had the same advantages. He pointedly warned those in power that oppressive rulers would fall without the support and contributions of the masses.

Response was immediate but limited. Officials and landowners tried to appease malcontents everywhere with small measures of improvement. The masses called for total attack on the social problems, and rioting was widespread; in Berlin, streets were barricaded against those trying to march on government buildings. Virchow was a ringleader of the attack against the government's do-little policy. For two years, he and a few friends published a journal, *Die medizinische Reform,* in which they campaigned for the establishment of a ministry of health, a reformation of medical education, and state support of medical students. Virchow and the others went even further by proposing measures that sound familiar today. They insisted that the state should care for any indigent citizen incapacitated by disease or old age.

For his audacious role in abetting the masses in their uprisings, Virchow's salary at the medical school was stopped. He was not publicly dismissed, but withdrawal of monetary support made it impossible for him to live or to work in Berlin. He was not without friends, however, and he accepted an invitation to Würzburg in 1849. There he continued his research with ever-deeper study into cellular structure; he held that cells dominate life and are the root of all disease, explaining that "illness is life no less than health. It is life under a modified condition. The cell is therefore the sustainer of both health and illness."

Virchow contended that any diseased condition of the kidney, for example, was due to a change in the cellular structure of that organ. If medical men wished to find the cause of a diseased kidney, he claimed that they must search for the reasons why the cells of the kidney changed. Convinced of the correctness of his theory, he was obstinate in his defense of it. He demolished with logical scientific fact and with the verbal invective of a tartar any who dared to disagree with him. Proofs demonstrated by his own research and his arguments were both so convincing that he swayed many sound scientists. Under his dominating leadership, outstanding medical researchers were forced to employ the mircroscope to examine minutely healthy and diseased organs in an effort to discover how and why cells change from normal to abnormal, producing diseases.

Virchow's scientific production, his far-flung fame, and his predominance in German medical circles gave him such distinction that he was invited to return to Berlin and, in 1856, was reinstated as a full member of the medical faculty. He encouraged his students to prove him wrong in any research results, if they could. When some few did find him in error, he accepted their results with disapproval tinged by respect.

Only a few years after his return to Berlin, Virchow was again in political disagreement with authority, this time with no less a figure than the mighty Bismarck. Virchow was opposed to Bismarck's ouster of Austria from Germany in 1862 and to the conflict in which Prussia triumphed over Austria in 1866. The Franco-Prussian War of 1870–71 found the scientist bitterly at odds with Bismarck's leadership and policies. Referring to him as a political dictator, Virchow once came close to calling him a liar in a public forum. Virchow served as an elected member of the Reichstag from 1880 to 1893 and was always a proponent of a socialistic state, an opponent of ironclad power for the few. His original proposals of social reform centered primarily on medical affairs.

While never neglecting his medical research, his direction of Germanic medicine, or the cause of socialism, Virchow was active in artistic, musical, and literary circles. Typically, he lauded those with creative and advanced ideas, and the impact of his comments, written or spoken, was far-reaching.

Virchow made a great art coup by securing for Germany the treasures from ancient Troy that had been excavated by Heinrich Schliemann, his intimate friend. Schliemann, born in poverty, early became interested in Homer's story of Troy, which he accepted as fact, not fiction. After he had earned a vast fortune, he dug at Troy as he had promised himself as a youth that he would do. When gold objects and other treasures were unearthed at Troy, Schliemann's Greek wife wanted him to give them to the government of her country. For numerous reasons, he hesitated to make a final decision. Then one day Virchow settled the matter.

Sitting quietly with Schliemann at the site of ancient Troy, Virchow plucked a blossom from a blackthorn and, handing it to the archaeologist, said, "A nosegay from Ankershagen," referring to the German village where Schliemann grew up. That nostalgic reminder of the past and appeal to his nationalism made Schliemann decide then and there to give the treasure to Germany not to Greece. Such subtle technique was characteristic of Virchow, but no one will ever know whether he deliberately trapped Schliemann into a decision favorable to the land of his birth. In any case, the credit goes to him.

Virchow was not a modest man. He was always aware of his own authority, prominence, and influence, particularly in the world of medicine. Toward the end of his long life, bacteriology, a science based on a new theory of bacteria as the cause of disease, was introduced, and he opposed its principles. He held firmly to his conviction that cells control all life. He failed to see that cellular and bacteriological theories of disease were little different. Since then, the science of bacteriology has progressed, contributing monumentally to medical advancement. Bacteriology *is* consistent with Virchow's elaboration of the cellular theory of health and diseases. The luster of his research is not dimmed by later discoveries that are in fact extensions of the foundations on which he placed building blocks essential to medicine today.

Before Virchow forced men to scrutinize life, disease, and death with scientific precision and detail, the laboratory had been neglected. Generalizations of clinical findings represented the philosophy of anatomy. Virchow's domination of the medical scene eventually led to the teams that today work in harmony in laboratory and clinic. Deserving the title "father of modern pathology," Virchow died in Berlin on September 5, 1902.

Kocher, the only surgeon to win a Nobel prize, studied the thyroid gland, devised an operation for its removal, and provided information about cures for diseases resulting from its malfunction.

Emil Theodor Kocher

1841–1917, *Swiss*

Today, after graduation from medical school, a young doctor enters a hospital for internship. If, as most do, he chooses a specialty, he continues with a long period of hospital residency during which he progressively assumes ever more responsibility. Through the supervised period of his residency, he perfects the techniques of his special medical area. The intern-resident system was not in effect when Emil Kocher graduated from medical school in Bern, Switzerland, in 1865. Then, most doctors received their degrees and went into practice without further training. Kocher, with a background of financial security, was able to travel to great medical centers in order to study with eminent physicians and surgeons who either had devised or practiced with the most advanced medical procedures. Kocher arranged his own internship and residency that were carried out in Paris and Berlin and, significantly, in London with Sir Joseph Lister and in Vienna with Theodor Billroth.

The Swiss doctor did not return to his homeland until 1870; he was twenty-nine on August 25 of that year. Kocher had been reared in an atmosphere of family contentment by parents of the upper middle class. His native city of Bern was a pleasant community, and Switzerland, at the time of his childhood as always, maintained its neutrality and provided a high standard of living for its citizens.

Kocher was a better than average student in all his schooling and completed his education with honors. It was his record of academic achievement that helped him to be accepted by the medical scholars with whom he studied in foreign capitals of Europe.

His London mentor, Joseph Lister, was the creator of antiseptic procedures for surgery, hospital therapy, and general practice. When Lister began his own practice, he was horrified by the number of patients who died from infections contracted after they had undergone routine and uncomplicated surgery that should have been highly successful. From observation and through reading, he began to understand why these patients died. He read Louis Pasteur's treatise, which stated that germs suspended in the air cause putrefaction. Those germs, Lister reasoned, could also exist on surgical instruments, on the catgut used for suturing after an operation, and on the hands of doctors. Lister often saw doctors go directly from dissecting a cadaver to the operating room without washing their hands or covering clothes that might be contaminated.

Having arrived at various potential causes of the gangrene that killed so many patients, Lister took precautions against them. He fought his battle for antisepsis, the prevention of infection, through the use of scrubbed hands, surgical gowns, sterile instruments, and cleanliness of all humans and each object that touched the patient. His colleagues laughed at Lister, but the low rate of death from infection in wards over which he had control was at length convincing proof that his theory was valid. For his work, he was knighted by Queen Victoria.

Kocher, working side by side with Lister, learned the procedures of antiseptic care of patients during surgery and postoperatively. He followed Lister's lead, and, during nearly a half century of surgical treatment of patients in Switzerland, he adhered to the principles of antisepsis and asepsis.

Kocher went to Vienna to observe the techniques of Theodor Billroth who was internationally known for his surgical skill. Surgeons, young and old, flocked to Vienna from around the world to watch, assist, and learn from the pre-eminent Billroth, an abdominal surgeon without peer. Most of the foreign doctors returned to their native lands, where they became the local masters of the surgical art. Young Kocher was lucky enough to be asked to stay on to work with Billroth. The older man sensed that Kocher had a creative medical mind and recognized his surgical adeptness. Kocher, already schooled by Lister in antiseptic techniques, was ready for the special attention given to him by Billroth.

Day after day, Kocher acted as assistant in the operating room and carefully followed the progress or decline of patients, resulting in either recuperation or death. He probed for the reasons for recovery or death. When not operating, Kocher was to be found hard at work: he tended postoperative patients in the wards; he conducted experiments in the laboratory; he studied cadavers in the dissecting room. Whether as assistant to Billroth or when performing operations himself, he was aware of those surgical instruments that were inadequate for certain procedures. In such free time as he could make for himself he tried to design better instruments for the improvement of surgical treatment. The Kocher clamp for clamping blood vessels is widely used today.

Kocher possessed a laudable combination of characteristics: modesty, daring, inventiveness. In November 1869, he wrote to a Swiss friend, saying,

"Throughout life one never ceases to learn from others, but there comes a time when a man must assume full responsibility for his actions and practice what he has learned. How simple it would be to remain in Vienna, cocooned in Billroth's protective womb and remain with him for life. Yet, I feel uneasy. My heart urges me to return home and share what I have learned with others while I administer to the ill."

This uneasiness erupted into action in 1870, and he returned to Bern to "assume full responsibility for his actions" and to practice what he had learned. In his native city, he began to make the contributions to humanity and to medical progress that marked his life work. He was appointed director of the Surgical Clinic at the University of Bern, a post he held for forty-five years.

Kocher operated every day, constantly creating new surgical procedures or modifying well-established methods. Early in his career, he developed a new procedure for the reduction of a dislocated shoulder. He operated on diseased lungs, malfunctioning gall bladders, gross hernias, and cranial nerves. After advance thinking, he boldly used surgeon's instruments on areas of the body that were presumed to be inoperable. The cut of his knife was precise and its use practical. From the very start of his surgical career, he could have depended for fame on his skill in that one area of medicine. However, Kocher conducted laboratory research, too, seeking new facts about human pathology; he related to his own surgery various known approaches to medicine and the intricacies of both chemistry and bacteriology. He held that he could continue to contribute to surgery only with a wider knowledge of every facet of medicine because "each is like a cobweb, interrelated as a unit."

Kocher's study of the thyroid gland transcends all of his other accomplishments, however outstanding. The thyroid is a ductless gland composed of two soft lobes; tissue, connecting the lobes, passes across the trachea at the front of the neck. The thyroid, although it is no larger than a child's thumbnail, produces hormones that are distributed throughout the body where they regulate various bodily functions.

Kocher's research into thyroid problems was sparked by his interest in and sympathy for persons afflicted with *cretinism* and *myxedema,* two forms of the same disease.

Cretins, congenitally deformed, are monstrous little individuals of a type known to have existed since the beginning of history. They are erroneously called dwarfs because they are so little. They have wrinkled faces even when young and short legs that appear to be incapable of supporting their thick bodies. Cretins, who have bulbous bellies and massive heads, have idiotic facial expressions; they look dull-witted and, in fact, many are of a very low mentality.

Myxedema is common among adult women who are stunted neither physically nor mentally but who have dry skin, puffy faces, and often an ugly goiter under the chin. The ailment sometimes strikes adult men, but most often it is a female disease.

It is no wonder that Kocher had a great urge to correct both conditions. He sought means for successful surgery of the goiter, the thyroid enlargement, a procedure fraught with many potential dangers. Such an operation had previously been tried by surgeons only at times of dire emergency, when loss of the patient was inevitable from suffocation due to the goiter's pressure on the windpipe. The chief danger in goiter surgery was loss of gushing blood. The thyroid gland, small as it is, receives more blood than most other organs of the body. Hemorrhaging therefore is not only possible but probable. No method was known then for stemming the free flow of blood during thyroid operations, and many patients died during their course.

Another serious risk in the operation was postoperative speech loss. The nerves leading to the *larynx,* the voice box, are located close to the thyroid. A slip of the surgical knife might result in the severing of the speech nerve, rendering the patient voiceless for life. Kocher was aware, too, that Billroth had attempted the removal of enlarged thyroid glands only to have the patients go into fatal convulsions. It was also known that if chest muscles were touched during the operation, the patient sometimes suffocated.

Cognizant of various deterrents to successful thyroid surgery, Kocher went to his laboratory and to the postmortem room. Painstakingly he learned the precise location of every blood vessel leading into, out of, and around the location of an enlarged thyroid. Laboriously he correlated the location of chest muscles with those around the goiter. As he began surgery, he first

made certain that his knife did not sever the laryngeal
nerve. Then, after making the incision, he tied off
every blood vessel around the growth. "By some mir-
acle" that he could not explain, Kocher never encountered any incidence of the potentially fatal
convulsions of patients that had plagued his teacher
Billroth and other colleagues. Kocher performed his
first excision of a goiter in 1872; in the following
decade, he performed the operation more than a thou-
sand times. He described his techniques in papers for
medical journals and demonstrated his methods before
visiting foreign surgeons who were eager to return
home with a technique that could alleviate the physical
suffering and mental anguish of victims with thyroid
disorders.

Kocher, dedicated to sharing of his surgical experiences with other doctors, reported on the strange case of
a young girl whose goiter he had removed successfully.
Her recovery was rapid, and she returned to the Swiss
village where she lived. Then, a dreadful thing began
to happen. With passing time, the youngster, once
mentally alert, became dull-witted. She was physically
sluggish and, even worse, stopped growing. Other surgeons, reading Kocher's report of the unfortunate turn
taken by this patient, reported examples of the same
postoperative symptoms when the thyroid was removed.
Possible reasons for the condition were advanced at
municipal medical meetings and at international conferences. Kocher was not satisfied by any explanation.

He got in touch with former patients who had undergone thyroid surgery, and about forty Swiss cases returned for examination. Three-quarters, or thirty, of the patients evidenced some form of physical transformation. Some were tired all the time. Others suffered periodic loss of memory. A few adults had symptoms of myxedema: dry skin, thick eyelids, puffy lips; and, particularly among very young people, cretinism or stunted growth appeared. Kocher was considerably distressed and shaken by the results of his examinations of the former patients. He vowed to discover the cause of the postoperative complications, which indicated a distinct link between cretinism and myxedema and the thyroid gland.

Month after month he operated on animals, removing one thyroid lobe from one animal, the other lobe from a second, and both lobes from still another. Keeping detailed records of his own research and clinical experience and assembling the reports of other surgeons, he continued to perform thyroidectomies, removing part or all of the gland. By 1909, when he had completed thousands of these procedures, he reported that postoperative myxedema developed in all patients from whom he had removed the entire thyroid gland. No sign of impending or immediate onset of the disease had developed when one lobe or even a part of one lobe still remained in the patient.

Kocher, through his years of laboratory investigation and by experience with countless surgical excisions, learned how and why cretinism develops as a congenital condition and myxedema as a postoperative complication. Thyroid hormones control the rate by which the human body burns the food to be transformed into energy, and the thyroid must be normal for the control to work. In cases of congenital hypothyroidism, when babies are born with little or no thyroid gland, little or no hormonal secretion comes from the gland. This means that there is no control on the burning rate of the fuel, no energy regulator; so the bodily functions slow down, and cretinism is produced. In the case of total removal of the thyroid, some symptoms of cretinism develop because of the lack of hormonal secretion. The opposite of too little hormonal secretion is too much secretion, which produces a hyperthyroid condition. In that case, the body is forced to work excessively to produce fuel. Evidence of the condition in a patient is weight loss, eyes that bulge, muscle tremors, profuse sweating, and, frequently, goiter. Since Kocher's time, there have been great advances in the understanding of thyroid disorders and the care of patients suffering from them, but all progress dates from his painstaking research and the techniques he developed through years of experience.

Kocher received the Nobel prize in 1909 for his contributions to physiology, pathology, and, above all, for his thyroid-gland surgery.

Ferrier originated studies on localization of many functions of the brain and gave direction to neurologists for finding what part of the brain controls which parts of the body.

David Ferrier

1843–1929, *Scottish*

At an early age, David Ferrier put his brain to good use; it was that organ of the body that he later studied with definitive results. An unknown Scottish schoolmaster at a country post recognized in young David a boy of exceptional mental capabilities. He learned swiftly; retained what he was taught; and questioned many ideas that had long been thought to be incontrovertible. David was not in the slightest way pugnacious but quietly persisted in doubting things presented to him as fact. Never challenging anything openly or vociferously, the young pupil pondered his doubts and, for one so young, delved deeply into whatever idea or theory worried him. After long and considered thought, he laconically stated his opinion about the subject.

All teachers with sensitivity delight in an exceptional

pupil, and David's teacher was no exception. He encouraged the boy in his quest for knowledge and approved his determination to prove facts, his innate ability to use the experimental approach to the solution of every problem. Without doubt, Ferrier's future was assured in those formative years when his natural bent was fostered by the schoolmaster. In later life, Ferrier's creative contributions to the science of neurology were conceived and carried forward with the same steady and deep thinking that characterized the probings of schoolboy days.

Ferrier was born in 1843 not far from Aberdeen at the mouth of the River Dee in northern Scotland. The thriving seaport served incoming fishing fleets, outgoing cattle boats loaded with the famous beef of the region, and cargo vessels with farm and industrial products shipped by the thrifty Scots. Ferrier's family was part of a typical clan, living quietly, working diligently, and saving as scrupulously as they could. His middle-class parents were able to send David to the Universities of Aberdeen and Edinburgh. He received his doctor-of-medicine degree in 1870 and moved to London, where he spent the rest of his professional life.

By the time Ferrier reached London, he had decided to concentrate on the then emerging specialty of neurology, the study of the brain and its function of controlling the entire body. Within a decade after Ferrier began a private practice that was most successful, he became more interested in teaching and in developing experimental methods for brain study. In 1880, he joined the staff of the National Hospital and became a member of the faculty of the Medical School of King's College. His outstanding ability as a teacher was soon demonstrated. His students, many of whom later became leaders in the field of neurology, were in accord that his lectures were "precise, organized and proceeded from A to Z in a most logical and understandable manner. Yet, they were always stimulating, so that we left the lecture hall eager to put his ideas to experimental proof."

The phrase to "put to experimental proof" was repeatedly used by Ferrier and appeared in most of the numerous papers describing his experiments with the brain. As youth and man, Ferrier accepted nothing on hearsay or conjecture. Any fact or idea was always "put to experimental proof." He impressed the importance of this procedure on his students and colleagues; he demanded evidence of proof for himself and for others. Even before he left private practice, he had performed many experiments on portions of the brains of animals, using electricity and recording muscular responses to that stimulus.

In speech, Ferrier was direct and quiet-spoken; in build, tall and erect yet slight of frame. He was indefatigable and often worked in his laboratory around the clock without sleep. It was during those concentrated periods that he evolved his most memorable contributions to neurology. Although his contributions were great, he was modest and preferred to give credit to others when he might have taken it solely for himself. He wrote, "I am fortunate in being in my position at a time when much has been discovered about the functioning of the brain and nervous system. Employing facts already proved, I am enabled to find proof of a few more facts to add to the burgeoning science of neurology."

The four major parts of the brain were known: *medulla oblongata, cerebellum, cerebrum,* and *midbrain.* It had been partially proved that the brain is the control station for all nerve impulses and is composed chiefly of nerve cells whose fibers are interwoven into a complex relay system. The brain, weighing approximately forty-five ounces in an adult human being, and its interrelated nervous system are sensitive to changes in the exterior and interior of the body. The brain detects all kinds of stimuli and controls muscular movement, both voluntary and involuntary.

By experiment, Ferrier added information about the eighth to twelfth cranial nerves that rise from the spinal cord and extend into the medulla oblongata. The medulla oblongata, consisting of two sections, lies below the midbrain and above the spinal cord and is involved in the control of, among other functions, swallowing, vomiting, breathing, speaking, digestion, metabolism, and heartbeat. Large bundles of nerve fibers in the right half of the medulla oblongata transmit impulses to the left side of the body. If this right-side group of nerves is stimulated at one special point, a person moves his left arm; if the left-side group of nerve fibers is stimulated, the right arm moves.

This is but one of the many facts known about the motor stimulation controlled by the brain. Today, neurologists have mapped most of the areas of the brain that control not only our voluntary motor actions but the involuntary ones as well. In Ferrier's day much less was known, but he added significantly to the expanding knowledge of the brain, its function and action. William Mears, a contemporary and colleague, said that Ferrier "will be remembered and later lauded for his quietly daring and creatively conceived experiments in neurophysiology, experiments which established the concept of localization of functions controlled by the cerebrum, and for his leadership in evolving the science of neurology."

Mears was referring to experiments that led to proof that any electrical stimulation of a certain area of the brain's cortex produced movements or convulsions of a specific group of muscles related to that part of the nervous system. By repeated stimulation of minute areas of the brain, Ferrier began to map its motor action, confirming his theory and giving impetus to further studies.

He also demonstrated that if the area of the cortex that stimulated muscular action was removed surgically, the muscular area affected became paralyzed. That fact opened a new field that other medical scientists explored and led Ferrier himself to a study of tumors in the brain. After proving that beneficial results could be obtained through surgery, Ferrier urged neurosurgeons to perform operations and to explore the potential of brain surgery not previously attempted. Here his influence was monumental. Although he was not a surgeon, he inspired such confidence in others and offered such conclusive proof of his theories that surgical colleagues were willing to follow his instructions and advance their own therapeutic methods.

Ferrier put his ideas and hypotheses to experimental proof by experimenting with animals from tiny mice to man-sized apes. He was castigated for this aspect of his research by laymen who read about his experiments in the daily papers. Eventually, antivivisectionists brought criminal charges against Ferrier, and he was forced to stand trial. Records of the courtroom procedure make fascinating reading. Ferrier stood tall on the witness stand and with logical and completely calm statement proved beyond doubt that his experimental animals suffered no pain. He lucidly recounted discoveries made through animal experimentation and explained how those specific discoveries had saved human lives.

Ferrier was as thorough as in everything else he did, from teaching to detailed research. He was abundantly prepared for verbal examination and cross-examination. Before his trial, he had learned that four of his opponents, the antivivisectionists, had suffered and

been cured of diseases that could only have been conquered through facts established by experimenting on
animals. With devastating directness, but in a most
courtly manner, he asked, "Gentlemen, would you
rather have had these experiments performed on you?"
When he was cleared of all the charges, Ferrier showed
no outward rancor and shook hands with those adversaries intelligent enough to recognize their own lack
of understanding of the procedures of medical research
with animals.

Ferrier was in great demand as a consultant for both
private physicians, who treated patients with brain
disorders, and neurosurgeons, who dared to operate on
those with cerebral diseases. He encouraged young
men whom he considered to be capable, teaching and
training them through long hours when he disregarded
the passage of time. He was assiduous in attendance at
scientific meetings but avoided controversial exchange
at sessions that often became stormy and violent. Ferrier was above polemics.

In recognition of his contributions to medicine, he
was knighted Sir David Ferrier in 1911 by George V,
King of England. Asked to comment on his knighthood, Ferrier replied, "It is accepted with gratitude and
shall be borne with a sense of responsibility, since I
am only one of many who share the vision of a science
to which we all have devoted our lives." Such a statement from him was not one of mock modesty. He had
"put to experimental proof" the fact that he was a

part of an international group then centered in England, which was extending the frontiers of knowledge of the human brain.

Ferrier not only delved into the motor response and actions of brain and body, he probed the sensory areas. Although he was unable to carry his research here to proven conclusions, he held to the idea that there is total interaction between the motor and sensory areas of the brain. When other medical men vehemently claimed that the motor and sensory areas of the brain were separate and distinct entities, he remained calm, at odds with their point of view but not argumentative. We know now that Ferrier was correct; his disbelieving colleagues were wrong.

While in his own time Ferrier was recognized as a a leader in medical research and was honored by the knighthood, he subsequently was neglected somewhat by medical historians and writers on scientific subjects. Today, at last, he is being accorded his rightful place in the vanguard of those who successfully explored the brain. Neurologists and other medical experts recognize Ferrier's contributions as invaluable and essential to their own techniques of therapy and research.

Ehrlich's famous Magic Bullet was just one of four contributions he made to medicine during a lifetime centered solely on professional matters.

Paul Ehrlich

1854–1915, *German*

Silesia, both Upper and Lower, was long the center of a tug-of-war between Prussia and Austria, which were engaged in a power play for possession and domination of this potentially rich industrial area. It was to Upper Silesia that Rudolf Virchow went with a medical team to study the plight of workers trapped by the circumstances of the Industrial Revolution. The industrialized region was stabilized ultimately by a temporary settlement of areas controlled by Prussia and Austria. When Paul Ehrlich was born in the tiny Silesian town of Strehlen on March 14, 1854, that community had the outward appearance of a sleepy village; it was actually industrially active and educationally vital.

In contrast to most of the other medical scientists included in this book, Ehrlich was born into a family with scientific interests. His mother's family included five men of science. His cousin, Karl Weigert, was a well-known pathologist, and Paul, as a child, spent many hours with him discussing the study of diseases of the body. At nine, Paul was permitted to experiment in the physics laboratory of his paternal grandfather, who had been a provocative teacher of physics and botany. With him, Paul took long country walks on which he learned the fundamentals of botany. Influenced by his association with his various relatives and by the competent teachers with whom he studied at Strehlen, Paul was intellectually mature beyond his years. By the time he received his medical degree from the University of Strasbourg, he had studied also at the Universities of Breslau, Freiburg, and Leipzig. A year after his graduation from medical school, Ehrlich, at the age of twenty-five, became prominent at the Medical Clinic in Berlin. In recognition of his ability, he was given a free hand to carry out original research projects.

As a student, he had astounded the medical world with his research into the coloring of cells with dye. Those investigations were the first of four outstanding facets of research that represent the segmented professional life of Paul Ehrlich. Each provided scientists with revolutionary concepts in the field of histology, that branch of science dealing with the microscopic examination of vegetable and animal tissue in an effort to discover the organization of that matter. He also led the way in immunology and chemotherapy, treatment and cure of disease effected by chemicals.

Fundamentally, Ehrlich revived the theory of Paracelsus that chemistry is the basis of all medicine. Ehrlich's own concept was that each type of living cell, including bacteria and parasites, has a unique affinity for a particular substance. To test his theory, the young scientist placed various dyes on many kinds of animal cells and, by studying the stained cells under the microscope, saw clearly that different tissues responded in different ways to the same dye. Developing the examination still further, he demonstrated that one type of cell responded to one dye but not to others; each, he concluded, had a reaction, an affinity to a specific dye.

When Ehrlich started his experimentations, only fresh blood had previously been examined under the microscope. Ehrlich, drying a thin layer of blood on a glass slide, then stained the dried blood, heated it, and observed it under the microscope. The blood cells were clearly colored. This increased the clarity and extent of laboratory examinations of blood samples.

At that time, the German scientist Robert Koch, having isolated the tubercle bacillus, the germ that causes tuberculosis, had invented a tuberculin test in order to diagnose the disease. The difficulty encountered by any investigator was that with the microscopes available in that day the germ was often difficult to see and to identify. In 1882, Ehrlich announced a new and "beautifully simple technique" for viewing the tu-

bercle bacillus under a microscope. After repeated trials
with numerous dyes, he arrived at a technique for staining blood with an aniline dye and an acid discolora-
tion. When the mixture was applied to blood, any tuberculosis bacilli present could be seen clearly, even if
mixed with other bacilli. With certain refinements, that
technique is still used today. That was the first major
contribution of a young man who in his lifetime un-
covered many more facts of value to the medical world
and to the patients suffering from diseases.

As has been said, Ehrlich was convinced of the prime
importance of chemical substances to diagnosis and
therapy. His staining techniques provided the basis for
chemical analysis of body tissues, both living and dead.
In rapid succession, he applied his staining processes
to a series of different kinds of body cells, making possible the diagnosis of a wide range of pathological conditions. He showed that white corpuscles of the blood
have an affinity for different substances. When the white
corpuscles were stained with three dyes, they could be
broken down into five different types by their reaction
to the dyes, thus permitting broader diagnostic study.
He also discovered that white blood cells play a vital
role in the function of bone marrow, the soft tissue that
fills the cavity of the bone.

By correlating of the portion of the body and the dye
for which it had affinity, Ehrlich opened up many new
fields of study. In 1886, he injected a mouse with the
dye substance known as methylene blue. Dissecting the

mouse, Ehrlich found that the methylene blue went directly to the nerve ends and nowhere else in its body. The nerve ends had an affinity to the methylene blue; thereafter, doctors intent on their study used injections of methylene blue to advance the research.

As Ehrlich proceeded at high speed but always with scientific care, he coined names for cells, reactions, pathological conditions, and processes that came to light for the first time as a result of his staining techniques. His work, heralded in the medical world, advanced the study of the normal histology and morphology of the body; opened the way for modern investigations in hematology; and made possible the rapid development of bacteriology and pathology, especially in the diagnosis of such blood diseases as anemia and leukemia.

Ehrlich was a quiet man who, without a trace of arrogance or egoism, had complete confidence in his own mental ability. He devoted himself completely to laboratory investigation and was uninterested in politics, cultural advancement, or social pleasures. Medicine was his life, and he lived it with a zealous conviction that not one moment should be wasted on any pursuit other than delving for facts to aid human beings beset with diseases. Pushing himself beyond his own physical limits, he contracted pulmonary tuberculosis in 1887 and was forced to spend a year in Egypt. He recovered his health while his active mind worked out problems without the aid of laboratory instruments on which he had so long depended.

In 1896, Ehrlich was appointed to the staff of a newly established scientific research institute in Steglitz, not far from Berlin. There he began investigations in immunology. Using bacterial and chemical methods, he studied the phenomena and causes of immunity from diseases.

He made one notable study after consultation with Emil von Behring, the German bacteriologist who had only recently discovered the antitoxin for diphtheria; in 1901, Behring was awarded the first Nobel prize for medicine in recognition of his discovery of the antitoxin. A toxin is a poison formed as a specific secretion in the metabolism of a vegetable or animal organism. An antitoxin, a serum produced and introduced into the body, fights and destroys the toxin, thereby producing in the body an immunization against the specific disease caused by a specific toxin.

After considering Behring's work with an animal antitoxin, Ehrlich demonstrated that an antitoxin can also be effective against plant poisoning. Selecting three plant toxins, he ultimately proved that they followed the same rules of immunization as those produced by bacteria toxins. This discovery, almost a by-product of his research, was later to have tremendous effect on the vital field of immunization against many diseases attacking the human body.

Not content with his initial investigations, Ehrlich produced a powerful antitoxin serum that immunized horses from several equine diseases. He injected a toxin into a horse until a serum was obtained with the exact antitoxic degree necessary to immunize the animals. Carrying his research to greater refinement, he charted the course of rhythmic and repeated injections of specified quantities of antitoxin to provide temporary or permanent immunity against several diseases. With this achievement, Ehrlich established the foundation for contemporary quantitative methods of immunization against disease. Anyone who ever is vaccinated against smallpox or who takes a series of typhoid shots or a tetanus booster is profiting from the research done by Ehrlich.

Concentrating his research techniques on pregnancy, childbirth, and breast feeding, Ehrlich startled the medical community by showing beyond any doubt when the mother is immunized against a disease, she transmits the immunization to the infant sucking milk from her breast.

The third segment of Ehrlich's professional life began with the postulation of a theory of immunity that he arrived at through an intensive study of his own massive and detailed records of toxin and antitoxin experiments. He knew that every cell has several receptors, receivers that normally accept and admit into the cells the sustenance required by them. If toxins attack and are admitted to the cells, the receptors and other cellular parts are destroyed. However, the receptors are so vital that they renew themselves faster than they can be destroyed by the toxin. From his laboratory results, Ehrlich was led to suggest that when an increased amount of toxin enters the body and combines with the cell receptors, the numerical production of receptors is rapidly increased. Because of the excessive production, the receptors are detached from the cells and pass freely into the fluids of the body, ultimately reaching the blood stream.

Ehrlich painstakingly followed the procedure through and found that as more toxin enters the body it is greedily accepted by the free-floating receptors. These eventually are destroyed and pass out of the body in urine or excrement. In that way the original organism becomes immune to the particular poison that originally attacked the cellular structure of its body.

Experimenting with animals, Ehrlich discovered by trial and error the right amount of toxin to be administered at calculated intervals. He learned that complete immunity results from proper dosage given in proper sequence. This side-chain theory was of immeasurable importance to the development of techniques of immunization that were carried to conclusion by other medical experts.

With his immunization research completed to his satisfaction, Ehrlich began another study that resulted in a triumph of chemotherapy. This was the fourth and most prestigious segment of Ehrlich's professional life.

At that time, a fatal disease known as trypanosomiasis, sleeping sickness, was rampant in Africa. Victims first had high fevers accompanied by an extremely rapid pulse beat. That stage of affliction was followed by an inability to walk and impaired speech; eventually, the bedridden patient died. It was known that the disease was carried by the tsetse fly, and the parasitic organism trypanosome was isolated as the cause of the devastating disease.

Ehrlich returned to the dye experiments of his early life. He endeavored to find a dye that would stain only the trypanosomes, so that they might be detected before sleeping sickness became virulent. He hoped that it might be possible to discover an antitoxin for immunization against trypanosomiasis. Unfortunately, he failed in his early attempts to control or immunize against the disease. Yet the direction of his experiments led to diagnostic and therapeutic successes with other diseases. He learned from colleagues that atoxyl, a monosodium salt of p-arsanlicid (from arsenic), had destroyed trypanosomes in the laboratory. However, it created the side effect of blinding the experimental animals on which it was used. Intuitively, Ehrlich decided that by changing the atoxyl molecule he might destroy the trypanosomes without creating other complications. He changed the atomic structure of the molecule and injected it into mice. New side effects appeared.

Year after year, Ehrlich and his assistants persisted in their search for a solution to the problem. The results of their experiments frequently surprised them. Once, mice injected with a newly arranged molecule of atoxyl suddenly began a mad, dervishlike dance in their cages. The tiny animals whirled, turned, jumped, scampered, and cavorted until they fell from exhaustion. The experiments went on and on until literally hundreds of atoxyl-molecule arrangements had been tested.

Finally, Ehrlich and his associates created the 606th rearrangement of the molecule. The formula worked. It destroyed the trypanosomes in mice, guinea pigs, and other animals without side effects. The chemical name for the substance is dioxy-diamino-arseno-benzene, popularly known as salvarsan. After the success that had come after such a long period of experimentation, Ehrlich pondered about the potential efficacy of salvarsan in the cure of syphilis. He knew that syphilis was caused by a *spirochete,* a slender, undulating microorganism that is a member of the Order *Spirochaetales,* many of which cause disease. The one causing syphilis is known as *spirochaeta pallida.*

Ehrlich wondered whether the salvarsan, or 606 as it also was called, that could kill trypanosomes could also kill spirochetes, establishing a cure for syphilis. He infected rabbits, mice, and chimpanzees with the disease, and when the characteristic sores appeared, the animals were given proper dosages of 606 by injection. The sores gradually disappeared in a matter of weeks. Word of Ehrlich's experimental coup spread. Doctors begged for 606 to inject into syphilitic patients. Ehrlich was reluctant to place salvarsan on the commercial market but, since his life had been devoted to the elimination of human disease, he granted permission for 606 to be tested on human beings.

In April 1910, he received reports of the controlled tests with 606, called the Magic Bullet because of its property of going straight to the target. In most cases, the substance cured syphilis, but a long series of treatments with repeated injections was required. Some patients died. Autopsy was ordered after every death, and the cadaver was studied carefully; in each case it was found that the drug had been mishandled. Administered with care by skillful physicians, salvarsan became the standard treatment for syphilis until penicillin provided a faster cure.

With his discovery, testing and application of salvarsan, Ehrlich provided the medical profession with an example of what chemotherapy could do. At a 1913 congress in London, he presented his views on and projection for chemotherapy, stating that more advanced research and testing would show that the *intravenous* (directly into veins) injection of chemicals eventually would cure many infectious diseases. His work, his success, and that particular lecture signaled the swift advance of chemotherapy.

While experimenting with dyes for diagnosis, antitoxins for immunity, and chemicals for the treatment of diseases, Ehrlich quietly invaded other medical fields. He performed vital experiments with many forms of malignancy; although this work was a side issue for him, he directed attention to the fact that *carcinoma,* a form of cancer of the epithelial tissue, may show all the manifestations of *sarcoma,* a fleshy malignant growth derived from nonepithelial tissue.

On a vacation, he saw a man die from a snake bite; back in the laboratory, Ehrlich demonstrated how venom affects the blood. He also identified *aplastic anemia,* now known as Ehrlich's anemia. Many of the pathological problems he investigated, were solved by him; others served as guidelines for the medical research of other men.

Ehrlich repeatedly told his colleagues, mostly students whom he had trained, "Waste not one hour because there is never time to accomplish the things demanded of you by humanity." He lived by that credo. In 1908, when he accepted the Nobel prize, he reiterated it as advice to any young men who wanted assiduously to aid their fellow men and to carry the science of medicine to greater heights. His only regret was that "I shall not live to see the wonders performed within the next fifty years. What we do today will be nothing compared to what will be accomplished soon."

He himself trained so many leaders of medical science that "Ehrlich's school" is a not uncommon term. He lived to hear many of his students praised, but not Gerhard Domagk who, using Ehrlich's methods, discovered sulfanilamide and was awarded the 1939 Nobel prize for that feat.

Paul Ehrlich died unexpectedly in Hamburg on

August 20, 1915, at the age of sixty-two. The very day he died, he worked in his laboratory and animatedly discussed with associates the research he planned for the years ahead.

Abel, *a prophetic scientist, described the future course of medicine, built the first artificial kidney, crystallized insulin, and extracted hormones from an endocrine gland.*

John Jacob Abel

1857–1938, *American*

It was a long way from a farm near Cleveland, Ohio, to the European laboratory of Paul Ehrlich but, against long odds, John Jacob Abel made the pilgrimage. Unlike Ehrlich, Abel had no relatives in the sciences. His farm family had emigrated to America from the Rhine Valley of the Palatinate, a state of the old German Empire. John Jacob was born on May 19, 1857, and spent his boyhood helping his father till the soil. At the local high school, the youngster was quick at mathematics, intrigued by chemical formulas and the study of rudimentary physics, and fascinated by Latin as an exercise of the mind. The piercing and provocative questions put to the class by a chemistry teacher inspired the pupil to seek further education. He had to try for it on his own, because his family, while living comfortably, had no funds for university tuition.

Undaunted, John Jacob Abel presented himself to authorities at the University of Michigan in 1876. Whoever interviewed him must have been impressed, because arrangements were made for his admission and for a job by which he could support himself. Even so, financing his education was difficult, and he left the University to become principal of the La Porte, Indiana, high school. There he taught Latin, mathematics, physics, and chemistry and was a strict disciplinarian to recalcitrant students who would rather have been behind a plow than a desk.

With the persistence and doggedness that characterized his later life, the young high-school principal frugally saved enough money to return to the University of Michigan and, in 1883, received his doctoral degree. Even while teaching in the high school and completing his studies at the University, Abel envisioned that the science of medicine of the future would be expanded far beyond the confines of anatomical studies and the diagnosis of human ailments. He told a friend that medicine was on the brink of a vast expansion *based on the correlation of all sciences with chemistry as a vital core.* There were few institutions in the United States where he could prepare himself for that expansion as broadly as he wished. His conception was prophetic; his action, immediate. After receiving his advanced degree, he went at once to the Johns Hop-

kins School of Medicine in Baltimore, Maryland,
where he spent an entire year with Dr. Newell Martin,
one of the world's leading physiologists. With Martin,
Abel acquired broad, fundamental training; he devoted long hours to daily study and to laboratory investigations.

With that training and experience, he sailed for
Europe where, charting his own educational course,
he spent seven years studying with those doctors who
were experimenting with and opening up new areas of
medicine. He often visited Ehrlich's laboratory and
was in Germany when Ehrlich proved that nerve ends
have an affinity for methylene blue. During long talks,
the two men discussed Ehrlich's theory that every portion of the anatomy has its own affinity for a specific
chemical. The bond of professional interests and of
friendship between the two lasted until Ehrlich's death.

Abel's peregrinations of study in depth not only
prepared him for a career in medicine but gave him a
broad scientific education. According to Dr. E. Ken-
nerly Marshall, Jr., a student of and later a longtime
colleague of Abel, "He was prepared for scientific
medicine in a way which in America was only recognized as the correct one some thirty years later."

The vital role that chemistry must play in future
medicine was always uppermost in Abel's mind; he
thought about the subject and talked about it constantly. His European letters to friends and colleagues
in the United States stressed the importance of med-

ical chemistry in training, research, and therapy. In one letter, he expressed his desire to return home to "get ready for the twentieth century." On the other hand, he wrote, "I cannot return until I am fully qualified, and the time is not yet at hand."

When he felt that he was ready, he returned. In 1893, he joined the medical faculty at Johns Hopkins. It is said that he never let a week pass without reminding students and colleagues that the human body is a "walking drugstore," a living supply of chemicals. His emphasis on chemistry in relationship to the medicine of the future seemed somewhat absurd to many. Today, experts realize that Abel was not an obsessed visionary but a prophet.

In addition to teaching, Abel, who was Professor of Pharmacology, worked diligently in the laboratory. In Europe, after consultation with Kocher, he had become convinced of the importance of Kocher's thyroid research. Abel determined to do his own thyroid studies but abandoned them after the publication of the advances made by Hans Baumann in the study of iodine-containing iodothyroglobulin, which led to successful thyroid therapy.

Abel's own original investigation had centered on the endocrine glands and the isolation of their hormones. It was not then known that the key to many problems connected with each endocrine gland is found in the isolation of its pure active hormone, but

Abel did realize this, and his statements on the subject were far in advance of his time. In one address, he said,

> "The actual finding of definite and specific chemical principles in the organs of internal secretion has in each case an importance in the way of explaining and correlating a large number of disconnected facts, only to be likened to the discovery of the etiological state of an infectious disease."

Abel was much interested in the *adrenal medulla,* an endocrine gland that under certain circumstances raises the blood pressure. In 1897, he isolated the hormone of the adrenal medulla in the form of a benzoyl derivative. This was the first time an endocrine hormone was isolated, but it had not been isolated in its pure form. When that was done, the substance was called epinephrine, or adrenalin.

Today, no hour passes in any large metropolitan hospital without some patient receiving an injection of epinephrine. It gives dramatic relief to asthmatic patients and is a boon to those suffering from hives. The substance causes a marked constriction of blood vessels and is used thousands of times every day in connection with a local anesthetic for tooth extraction and repair and for innumerable minor surgical corrections.

In Canada in 1921, Sir Frederick Banting and his assistant, Charles Best, isolated the hormone insulin from the pancreas. That feat fired the imagination of

Abel who felt certain that he could obtain the hormone in a chemically pure crystalline form. He did exactly that in 1926 at the age of sixty-nine by using what one of his students had called "his quaint and antiquated methods of chemical procedure." Abel's first crystals are preserved and may be seen at Johns Hopkins.

His announcement of the crystallization of insulin as a final proof of the isolation of the pure hormone was received with skepticism by many chemists; they claimed that the highly potent pure hormone was adsorbed *on* a crystalline protein. Abel set about to satisfy his detractors, but something went wrong with his experiments; for several months he was unable to produce another quantity of insulin crystals. Calm and unflurried by the rumbles of rising criticism and doubt, Abel continued experimentation until he could repeatedly and consistently produce the substance. Criticism was quieted; doubts were dispelled.

In 1913, Abel envisioned a method of drawing human blood from the body, passing it through an exterior machine, and then introducing it back into the body at another point. His first discussion of the project is vividly clear to Dr. Marshall, who was later to become the Professor of Pharmacology and Experimental Therapeutics at Johns Hopkins. With the staff called together for lunch, Abel used small bits of bread to illustrate the piece of apparatus he had in mind, a construction to be called an artificial kidney. Abel explained how valuable the apparatus would be in re-

moving deterimental substances from the body and in
relieving the kidneys of their function at a critical
time. With enthusiasm, he fashioned an apparatus
made of metal and rubber tubing. For his first tests, he
used an experimental rabbit. The object of the experiment was to take arterial blood from the rabbit and
pass it through a series of tubes surrounded with a
saline solution and back into one of the animal's veins.
The procedure was perfected after many attempts.
Once established, the technique did not fail Abel as
his original experiment with the crystallization of insulin had. The artificial kidney worked every time.

Even after he had proved conclusively that the apparatus worked, many medical men thought him rash
to speak of its potential use with human patients. His
artificial kidney never was used on human beings, but
its principle was the basis for an apparatus tried on
three patients in Germany in 1926. Good results were
obtained in all three cases. Technical improvements
continued, and a doctor in Holland and one in Canada
made workable pieces of apparatus generally available.
Abel was generously thanked for his pioneering work
by his scientific peers in Germany, Holland, and Canada.

While Abel was experimenting with his artificial
kidney on dogs, he found that extremely large quantities of blood could repeatedly be withdrawn from the
animals *if* the red corpuscles of the blood were separated
and reinjected in a salt solution. In a 1914 paper on

this phenomenon, he wrote the following foresighted sentence,

> "In view of the fact that mammalian corpuscles retain their stability for three or four days when kept on ice, a supply of human corpuscles might possibly be kept in this manner in operating rooms for rapid injection in emergencies that would otherwise prove fatal."

That was the fundamental principle of the blood bank. In later conversations with surgeons and hematologists, Abel discussed the potential and predicted that the day would come when stored human blood would be administered to patients by a commonplace technique as routine medical procedure. Today, the blood bank is a reality and transfusions routine.

There were no limits to Abel's curiosity about the workings of the human "walking drugstore." Always optimistic, even when his research seemed at the brink of failure, he was cheerful and confident that at length he would succeed totally or partially in achieving results from his probings into unknown areas. He was not fazed by partial results because he had faith that others proceeding with the work would carry it to totally successful conclusion. A modest and unassuming scientist, he had complete assurance about the value of his work to the future of medicine, and he had no doubt that what he failed to finish would be done by later generations of scientists. Late in his life Abel wrote, "Greater even than the greatest discovery is to keep open the way to future discoveries." By that credo he lived, contributing things of immediate value and opening the doors through which others would walk.

Sulfa drugs were just beginning to be used a couple of years before Abel died. He followed the progress of research on those drugs and expressed his conviction that they would completely revolutionize the treatment of infectious diseases. On Christmas Eve, 1936, he was in his laboratory talking with Dr. Marshall about the sulfas. When Marshall was about to leave, Abel, looking pensive, said suddenly, "My God, Marshall, wouldn't Paul Ehrlich turn over in his grave." Ehrlich's dream of the conquest of infectious diseases by chemotherapy was coming true.

Abel himself regretted that he would not live to have all of his professional dreams come true. He was still working, planning and forecasting chemical treatment of human beings, those "walking drugstores," when he died on May 26, 1938.

Carrel was the first to sew blood vessels together, to keep body tissues alive in jars, to transplant animal organs, preparing the way for cardiovascular surgery and human-organ transplants.

Alexis Carrel

1873–1944, *French*

In the fifth century B.C., the Greek physician Hippocrates wrote, "It should be possible to replace diseased organs of the human body with healthy ones from a person recently decased." Sporadically throughout the following centuries, men of science tried to devise methods for organ transplants and for sewing together blood vessels, a technique that had to be refined before transplants could be effected successfully. Alexis Carrel was the first man to succeed with both surgical procedures. The accomplishments won fame and honors for an outstanding scientist who, disgraced in the eyes of his peers and fellow countrymen, died in ignominy.

Carrel was born on June 28, 1873, at Lyons, the French city at the confluence of the Rhone and Saône rivers that is second only to Paris as an economic center.

It was the birthplace also of André Marie Ampère, the French physicist for whom the electrical unit the *ampere* is named. Lyons, long famous for its cathedrals and museums, was a wealthy community with a high level of educational and cultural opportunities. In that atmosphere, the precocious Alexis Carrel was brought up. He decided at the age of twelve that he would be a doctor, and at sixteen he entered the University of Lyons. Like John Jacob Abel, Carrel thought that his preparation for medicine should be broad in scope. For that reason he first took a bachelor of letters degree, then a bachelor of science degree, and finally, in 1900, the degree of doctor of medicine. He served his medical internship at Lyons and taught anatomy and surgery at the University of Lyons for four years.

While Carrel was still a medical student, he was intrigued by the possibility of transplanting organs and read all the medical literature on theoretical methods and proposed techniques. Suturing blood vessels, the correlate procedure essential to transplantation, had been the subject of much talk and little experimentation, none successful. Carrel's own first attempts were made with techniques suggested in the works of other surgeons. Working with live dogs and cadavers, he severed blood vessels and repeatedly failed to find a way to stitch them back together again.

Sewing blood vessels presents many problems: Infection has to be avoided. The severing must be done neatly so that the ends are not torn. Vessels must be kept moist, not allowed to dry out. There should be no narrowing of the vessels at the point of suture because the stitching must permit normal expansion and contraction to prevent clotting of the blood. Blood has to flow freely past the point of suture on its routine circulation through the body.

Unable to achieve all of the requirements, Carrel experienced failure after failure. Discouraged, he migrated to Canada with the intention of renouncing a career in medicine for the lucrative business of cattle raising. But the challenge he had given to himself was too strong, and he accepted an invitation to work at the University of Chicago where he studied more physiology. His dedication to the development of much-needed vascular suturing impressed many American medical experts. In 1906 Carrel joined the research staff of the Rockefeller Institute for Medical Research.

Aided by the availability of funds and equipment and buoyed by the encouragment of the Rockefeller staff, Carrel renewed his research on suturing blood vessels. Before resuming practical experimentation, he did extensive and precise studies of every potential complication. Then, slowly and persistently, he conquered the complicating factors one by one. At last, he successfully met his own challenge and perfected the procedure for suturing blood vessels.

Each operation followed a set pattern. First, he made certain that the area of operation was initially infection free, and then the blood vessel was aseptically

treated to prevent subsequent development of infection. In order to keep the tearing and injury to the
blood vessel at the irreducible minimum and to prevent excessive bleeding, Carrel used smooth forceps
and clamps rather than the more conventional sharp
instruments. He learned early in his experimentations
that the tissue of the inner lining of the blood vessel
dried and died quickly after cutting. To prevent that
condition, he kept the tissue humidified and moist,
sometimes by the insertion of moist air, more often
with application of vaseline to the membrane that
lined the interior wall of the blood vessel.

While operating, Carrel gently drew the severed
vessel ends together with as little stretching as possible.
Placing three stitches in the circumference of the blood
vessel, he pulled slightly on the circumference so that
the blood vessel took on a triangular shape. Then he
brought together the edges of each side of the triangle,
exactly matching the surface of one cut end with the
wall surface of the second cut end. Cautiously, he proceeded to make sure that the free ends were not folded
inward at the point of suture. Had the edges folded inward, they would have created tiny pockets for the
collection and clotting of blood, a hazardous condition.
To insure that there would be no clotting, he folded
the free edges of the vessels outward, uniting their lin-
ings. Before putting in the last suture, he removed as
much as possible of the protective coating of vaseline.

With the final suture secure, blood again flowed freely through the operated blood vessel.

While doing his research studies, Carrel discovered that a different technique was required for suturing a vein. The vein has thinner walls than the artery and requires more stitches for suturing. That fact has been borne out by subsequent experience with cardiovascular surgery.

As soon as Carrel was able to suture severed blood vessels routinely and consistenly, he turned to serious research in the field of organ transplants. First, he cut a portion of a blood vessel from an animal and inserted it into another part of the animal's vascular system. He advanced from that operation to removing entire organs from the animal's body and replacing them in their original locations. In these cases, his techniques were successful. Every attempt at transplantation of an organ from one animal into the body of another failed.

Throughout his most trying times in the laboratory, Carrel withstood mockery even from august medical scientists and remained faithful to his own challenge. He belongs in a prodigious company of giants of science, in other disciplines as well as medicine, whose original work has been derided by their peers. People, fearing the new tend to taunt the innovator and then to do an about-face when the idea they dubbed outlandish proved to be worthy. The detractors of Carrel had no choice but to take him seriously in 1912 when he received the Nobel prize in physiology and medicine "in recognition of his works on vascular suture and transplantation of organs." Up to that time, while most members of the Rockefeller Institute staff admitted to his genius and supported his efforts, the larger community of scientists considered him to be a bit mad.

At the outbreak of World War I, Carrel returned to France and was commissioned a major in the French Army Medical Corps. He soon had opportunity to use his suturing techniques on human beings, soldiers wounded in battle. In combination with the suturing process, he used the Carrel-Dakin solution, which was recognized as an effective antiseptic by his contemporary Henry D. Dakin, a foremost chemist. The solution was applied during surgical procedures and for irrigating and dressing wounds. Carrel developed a method by which the solution could be kept indefinitely in gauze on a wound, preventing the development of gangrene, that plague of battlefields throughout history. Often the use of the solution obviated the need for surgery. Carrel is credited with having saved numberless lives of wounded soldiers.

After World War I, he returned to the Rockefeller Institute and turned his full attention to research, new but related to his earlier studies. When it became known that he was going to experiment with keeping alive human tissue and organs after their removal from the body, many medical scientists were convinced that he was not just slightly mad, but insane. As before, he did not heed abuse that came from many directions.

He continued with his research and managed to keep arteries alive for weeks in laboratory containers. He cultivated a chicken heart in a glass container and kept it in repair and alive for five years.

Carrel's work attracted the attention of Charles A. Lindbergh, the first man to complete a solo nonstop flight across the Atlantic Ocean. The aeronautic expert and the surgeon did research together and, in 1936, invented a mechanical heart in the form of a perfusion pump. It kept a heart, kidney and spleen alive in glass containers in which artificial blood constantly circulated. Lindbergh and Carrel were co-authors of *The Culture of Organs,* a book in which they gave detailed information about their work and circumstantial predictions for the future of organ transplants.

In 1939 Carrel left the Rockefeller Institute and once more returned to France, where he became a leading member of the French Ministry of Public Health. In 1940, after the defeat of France by Hitler's forces, the Nazi-ruled Vichy government was formed, and Carrel was part of it, heading the new Foundation for the Study of Human Relations. The basic ideology of the foundation was that a superior order could be created to rule the masses of people with lesser minds. The elite corps, it was claimed, would know what was best for all other people and would direct their lives. Following the concepts of Nazi leaders, Carrel directed the foundation's research toward a realization of Hitler's vision of a master race. When France was liberated in 1944,

Carrel was charged with Nazi collaboration. He died that year, without honor in his own country and disgraced in the world of science.

Despite Carrel's political affiliations, he is today given a place of prominence in the annals of medicine. Socrates, philosopher of ancient Greece, stated, "Only time proves guilt or innocence, value or depravity. Time tells all." And Geoffrey Keller, a young California friend of ours, wrote in his high school newspaper, "It is important that we not allow ourselves to be told that one thing or man was all good or all bad. History is not black or white; we must shade the characters and events only when we know all the facts and the results."

Carrel's history is shaded, and on the bright side is his brilliant research. The suturing of blood vessels opened the way for modern surgery, for heart operations now performed every day to save the lives of patients. One correction he made possible involves a congenital malformation of the aorta, sometimes so constricted in one place that the supply of the blood does not reach the lower portion of the body in the time and amount needed. Not long ago, a person born with that malformation had a life expectancy of only about thiry-five years. In 1944, the very year Carrel died, Charles Crafoord performed the first operation on a patient with that vascular condition, which is known as narrowing of the aorta. The constricted area was excised and

Crafoord, using Carrel's technique, sutured the two cut ends of the aorta.

The same year, Alfred Blalock and Helen Taussig of Johns Hopkins, in order to repair another congenital heart malformation, devised the famous procedure known around the world as the *blue-baby* operation. This operative procedure rerouted the blood so that an infant with an abnormal circulation receives enough oxygen to insure an opportunity for a long and normal life.

In the past, people by the hundreds of thousands a year have died from malformations of the cardiovascular system and other heart ailments that can now be surgically corrected. Dozens of heart and blood-vessel operations are being evolved every year. Modern cardiovascular surgery is enjoying ever-greater success and higher survival percentages; the surgical techniques are giving new hope to patients who, in an earlier day, would have lingered as invalids with whatever cardiovascular malfunction they suffered.

It is impossible to erase from the list of medical achievements those of the Nobel prize winner who died under a shadowed cloud but who retains professional respectability because of the positive contributions he made to mankind.

Banting's notable research with insulin overshadowed other valuable work: his studies of the adrenal gland and silicosis and his pioneering efforts in aviation medicine.

Frederick Grant Banting

1891–1941, *Canadian*

In 1938, Richard Kuhn, a German chemist, was not permitted by government authorities to accept the Nobel prize. With Hitler in power the following year, A. Butenandt and Gerhard Domagk were restrained from accepting the award after notification that they were to receive it for their work in chemistry and medicine respectively. Boris Pasternak, a Russian author, refused the Nobel literature award of 1958 on orders from leaders in the U.S.S.R. In 1964, Jean Paul Sartre personally refused the Nobel prize for literature, the only record of voluntary refusal up to this time. But several decades earlier, Frederick Grant Banting contemplated refusing the Nobel prize when, in 1923, two of his research colleagues were not included in the honor.

Banting, another farm boy among the distinguished

doctors of history, was born on November 14, 1891, in the country near Alliston, Ontario, Canada. The youngest of five children, he was brought up in a devout family, early learning the simple verities of life. The farm routine and the daily chores to which he was assigned made him robust and strong. He was a fun-loving youngster, with a sense of humor and high spirits, active in athletics and the center of attention at all school activities. Yet he was not a good student, and none of his teachers had any reason to suspect that his mind was of fine caliber.

His parents hoped that he would become a minister when they sent him to Victoria College in Toronto. He registered for the preministerial course, but at the close of his first year informed his parents that he could not carry on under false pretenses. Frankly, he did not have the urge to join the ministry but hoped rather to become a doctor in order to devote his life to the sick. When he returned for his second year at Victoria, he enrolled for medical studies and almost overnight became a top-flight student. He had found the sphere of activity that awakened his latent mental powers. While completing clinical work under Dr. Clarence Starr, surgeon-in-chief at a Toronto hospital for children, Banting thought that he might specialize in orthopedics.

His medical training was accelerated when Canada entered World War I in 1914, and Banting was graduated from medical school in 1917, already a member of the Canadian Officers' Training Corps. On active duty, he served principally in hospitals set up just behind the fighting lines in Europe, operating unceasingly on wounded brought to the temporary field hospitals. In 1918, he himself was wounded and invalided to England where his wound became infected. Attending surgeons decided on amputation of his right arm, but Banting refused the drastic operation that would have ended his surgical career. He treated his own infected wound, and the arm was saved.

When peace was declared, Banting, returning to Canada, set up an office in London, Ontario. He waited for patients. None came. At the end of three months, he had collected only twelve dollars in fees. In order to support himself, he accepted a position as a lecturer at the University of Western Ontario Medical School, where he taught both physiology and anatomy as well as giving demonstrations in orthopedic surgery for the students. Every minute of his free time was spent in serious study of physiology, a subject in which he had to keep just a lesson or two ahead of his students.

The preparation for a lecture on the pancreas changed the course of Banting's career. Some investigators had indicated a connection between the pancreas and diabetes, then a debilitating and fatal disease. At the time, the ongoing symptoms of diabetes and the lives of those afflicted with it were controlled by a highly sophisticated and specialized diet designed to keep the body's sugar level as low as possible. In his cram session, Banting recalled a medical-journal article on the pancreas and turned to it. Of the experience, he later wrote,

> "On October 30, 1920, I was attracted to an article by Moses Barron in which he pointed out the similarity between the degenerative changes in the acinus cells of the pancreas following the blocked stage of the duct with gallstones. [*Acinus cells* secrete a digestive juice and are distinct from hormone-producing cells.] Having read the article, the idea presented itself to me that by ligating [tying off] the duct and allowing time for the degeneration of the acinus cells, a means might be provided for obtaining an extract of the *islet* cells free from the destroying influence of trypsin and other pancreatic enzymes."

Barron's article went on to describe the wizened appearance of the pancreas in sick people whose pancreatic ducts were blocked. Suspecting diabetes, Barron had checked and found no sugar in the urine. He found that when the ducts were closed in experimental animals, the cells died, except for those diamond-shaped cells clumped together into "islets," which remained. However, when the whole pancreas was removed, the experimental animal contracted diabetes, and its urine became full of sugar.

Banting pondered the phenomenon, and, fired by enthusiasm for a new idea, he asked a doctor friend to come to his room. Together, they discussed the article, talking over the potential just below the surface of the written words and wondering if Barron's observation might not contain the clue for eventual succor for diabetics. Late at night the friend left. Banting related, long after, how he tossed in his bed. Then he got up and scribbled on a note pad, "Tie off pancreas ducts of dogs. Wait six to eight weeks. Remove and extract." With these few words his great contribution to humanity began to take shape.

Banting was discouraged by talks with colleagues, who advised him to consult Dr. J. J. R. MacLeod at the University of Toronto, a man noted for his knowledge of the metabolism of sugar. Explaining the tentative theory evolved, Banting read the fourteen words he had written to MacLeod. Disinterested, MacLeod tried to discourage Banting. Undaunted, the younger man returned the following day and eventually persuaded MacLeod to allow him to try his experimental idea. Half-heartedly, he ultimately agreed to give Banting laboratory space, an assistant, and ten dogs. When he was about to leave on a trip to his native Scotland, he set as the deadline for Banting's completion of experiments the date of his own return from Edinburgh.

Banting, with Charles Best as his assistant, was forced to work against the calendar with no research funds, limited laboratory space, and just ten experimental animals. Best, the son of a country doctor, had spent his childhood going on rural rounds with his father. At the time he was only a third-year medical student, but he had a sound knowledge of physiology and the metabolism of sugars. He had even had some slight experience in measuring blood sugar. Banting and Best began their race against time in mid-April 1921. They lacked everything but creative genius and daring.

They tied off the pancreatic ducts of several dogs. For seven weeks they checked the urine of the dogs, almost daily, hoping that the pancreases had shriveled. Finally, Banting operated and was disappointed to find every pancreas in perfect condition. He operated again, carefully tying the ducts. He and Best waited before further surgical investigation. Then they found the pancreas in each of two dogs shriveled to about one-third normal size. Excitedly, but with extreme caution, they cut out the pancreas of each dog, mashed the two organs into bits, and mixed the matter with cold briny water and sand. Only then were they able to withdraw several drops of a substance to place in the vein of a dog with diabetes.

Banting's report of the experimentation fairly sparkles with a sense of crackling tension felt at that juncture of the research. Every half hour, the two experimenters took blood samples to get the sugar level. Almost miraculously, the sugar content dropped from 200 milligrams to 110 milligrams in each 100 cubic centimeters of blood. The condition of the dog was vastly improved, but time was running out, and there was much more to be done. All ten experimental dogs given to them by MacLeod had been used. Banting sold personal possessions to get money for the purchase of more animals.

By one method and then another and still another, the two young scientists extracted the substance they sought. They learned that if they administered too much of the pancreatic substance, the sugar in an animal's blood fell below normal. During their research, they proved that the protein-splitting activity of the enzyme of the pancreas killed the substance produced in the islets.

MacLeod returned on schedule from Edinburgh. He surveyed the work done, approved it, and began experiments with Banting and Best. MacLeod named the extracted substance insulin. The three investigators very soon realized that they needed the cooperation of a specialist trained in biochemistry and took on, as the fourth member of their research team, Dr. James B. Collip. Balancing, rearranging, lowering, raising and rebalancing the insulin, the four men stabilized the amounts needed and produced it in pure form, but not in crystalline form which Abel later was to do.

Now, the crucial test had to be faced. Would insulin prove to be efficacious in the treatment of human diabetics? With understandable trepidation, they selected as a test patient a boy of fourteen whose parents consented to the proposed treatment. The child was tall but weighed only sixty-five pounds, and in spite of the rigid diet to which he was restricted, he was losing his fight for life. Too enervated to care or probably even to know what was being done, the boy submitted to the injection of insulin. Within a matter of days, he was active, ebullient, and hungry. With his diet controlled, his weight increased. He was the first of millions of patients for whom insulin was the life-giving and life-sustaining drug.

The demand for insulin was tremendous. It was soon produced commercially, and diabetics around the world were taught how to inject themselves with the drug in proper dosages. No one of the four who took part in the discovery, testing, and original application of insulin received one cent from the commercial companies that produced it. The royalty rights were signed over to the University of Toronto, where the income is still being used in continued hormone research.

In 1923 the Nobel-prize committee announced that MacLeod and Banting were to be awarded the laureate in medicine for their insulin research. Banting was upset on two counts: The original idea had been his and his name appeared second in the announcement. And, while Best and Collip had contributed as equal partners in the foursome to the successful research, neither of them was mentioned for the award. Banting briefly threatened to decline the prize, but reason won over emotion. MacLeod and Banting accepted the award. The Nobel prize carries with it financial remuneration, and Banting gave half of his award money to Best; an undisclosed sum was given to Collip by MacLeod.

Banting's insulin research has overshadowed his

other valuable work. He studied the adrenal gland, explored silicosis, the occupational disease of miners and others exposed to certain mineral dusts, and pioneered in aviation medicine. It is ironic that, in 1941, when he was en route to England for a wartime conference on aviation medicine, Banting was killed in a plane crash at Newfoundland.

Fleming, Florey, and Chain, all working together in England, discovered penicillin and the method for producing it in quantity in the United States of America.

Alexander Fleming
1881–1955, *Scottish*

Howard Walter Florey
1898–　, *Australian*

Ernst Boris Chain
1906–　, *German*

A galaxy of British scientists gathered one evening in 1952 at the Royal Society of London, just a stone's throw from Piccadilly Circus. We were privileged to be among those present, having asked several great men of British science to appear on the first program ever to be telecast from the Royal Society. The British Broadcasting Corporation had invited us to present a series of three programs from London; these were kinescoped and sent by air to be shown within a week in the United States on *The Johns Hopkins Science Review*.

We opened the program, shown live to British viewers, while standing beside a bust of Charles II, King of England, who in 1662 gave the charter to this internationally prestigious Society. Membership is coveted by many but awarded to only a few of the world's leading scientists.

After the opening of the program, we moved across the lobby, introducing several scientists, among them Sir Alexander Fleming, a small white-haired man with bushy black eyebrows accenting a pair of twinkling eyes. Smiling, Sir Alexander said, in answer to our question about penicillin, "I just happen to have penicillin mold with me," and chuckling, added, "since you asked me to bring it."

He pulled from his pocket a small glass petri dish containing strains of the original penicillin mold that he discovered in 1928. While televiewers at home looked at a close-up shot of mold still alive and growing after twenty-four years, Sir Alexander, with spritely enthusiasm, told the story of the discovery and development of penicillin. The recognition of the unique quality of mold that formed in his laboratory followed years spent in the profession of medicine.

Alexander Fleming was born on a farm in Ayrshire, Scotland, on August 6, 1881. After attending school in a nearby village, he left the classroom at the age of fourteen and joined his brother in London. There, Alexander was employed first as a shipping clerk and, for seven years, worked at a series of miscellaneous jobs while thriftily saving money out of his meager wages. In 1902, he took medical examinations and won a scholarship to St. Mary's Hospital Medical School in London. Six years later, he was graduated with a bachelor-of-medicine degree.

His skill in research and brilliance in therapy won him many graduation honors, a position in the bacteriology laboratory of Professor Almroth Wright, and a year later membership in the Royal College of Surgeons. Fleming introduced Paul Ehrlich's salvarsan into England and was responsible for its use in medical therapy in that country. Although he left the bacteriology laboratory for private practice, he continued to do research, investigating many drugs and their potential use in the cure or immunization of diseases.

His practice was interrupted by World War I, during which he served with the British Medical Corps. He treated the wounded at field hospitals and was angrily frustrated by the prevalence of infection. Unaware of the work being done with the Carrel-Dakin solution at other combat areas, he had no means for absolutely protecting the wounded against the spread of infection. Carbolic acid was too strong for use on the type of infections he encountered. Unless the solution is in extreme dilution, it destroys white corpuscles, which permitted further attacks from infectious microbes.

Fleming tried numerous methods for reducing infection including blood transfusions.

Deeply disturbed by his inability to save the lives of men who died not from bullet wounds, but from infection, Fleming changed the emphasis of his professional work after the war. He accepted a position as assistant director of the Inoculation Department of St. Mary's Hospital and professor of bacteriology in St. Mary's Medical School. In his research, like his predecessors and colleagues in the field, he had many failures. Once, he thought he had found what he was looking for, an antitoxic enzyme; it was present in egg white and several bodily fluids. But the *lysozyme,* a dissolved enzyme, while it did kill some bacteria, was ineffectual against bacteria that cause dangerous diseases.

Entering the laboratory one morning, Fleming glanced at the many petri dishes in which he was growing bacteria. The appearance of the substance in one dish was strikingly different from the others. Obviously some foreign substance had blown in through an open window and settled on the mold in the petri dish. Fleming was about to throw out the contaminated material when, through a stroke of good luck and as a result of long training in research observation, he paused. Taking a thin piece of platinum wire, he extracted a bit of mold and placed it under his microscope. His intuitive sense alerted him to the fact that he was viewing something unique on the microscope slide.

While he watched, fascinated, a circle of fluid grew and floated around the bacteria. Swiftly, the bacteria disappeared; they were being destroyed before his very eyes.

With the help of his laboratory assistants, he extracted more mold from the contaminated petri dish and dropped it onto another dish in which *staphylococci* germs were growing. Within a few hours the filtrated mold had killed the staph germs. On examination Fleming found that the mold belonged to the vast family of *Penicillium,* microbes that induce rotting of apples and oranges and give color and pungency to roquefort cheese. Elated, he and his laboratory aides diluted the moldy liquid to one part mold in 100 parts water. Even this solution killed staphylococci. Making a solution of 800 parts water, the experimenters found that the mold liquid was even more potent than carbolic acid. The highly diluted liquid destroyed the deadly germs of *streptococci* and *pneumococci* within a few hours.

Fleming experimented widely with the mold solution in varying strengths. It had no effect on the germs causing typhoid or on those attacking the intestinal tract; it did kill germs of the staph, strep, and pneumo variety. One of the many questions raised by the mold solution was whether or not the new substance would damage white corpuscles. Fleming injected the drug into blood serum drawn from animals. The white corpuscles remained undamaged. He had discovered a substance that was as potent as carbolic acid but without the often devastating side effect of causing tissue damage. Fleming named the drug penicillin.

A major problem remained. Somehow penicillin would have to be produced in amounts large enough for the treatment of human patients. In 1929 Fleming read a report and published a paper giving his account of the potency of the drug and presenting the seemingly insuperable problem of its preparation in any practical quantity. No drug company came forward. There was no government assistance nor offers that would accomplish what was needed to provide the world with penicillin treatment. For ten years this discovery was only a laboratory success, and then two other scientists opened the way for its testing and universal use.

Howard Walter Florey, born September 24, 1898, in Adelaide, Australia, and Ernst Boris Chain, born June 19, 1906, in Berlin, Germany, were fated to be an experimental team of scientists. Florey emigrated from Australia to England where Chain had settled after fleeing from Nazi oppression in Germany. Both men were interested in the same area of medicine, drugs that would kill bacteria causing illness and often death. They began to work together at Oxford University in 1935. Their research was broadly based, dependent on their own theories and on those of predecessors in many countries.

It was Florey who, recalling a paper published ten years earlier in the *British Journal of Experimental*

Pathology, reread Fleming's report on penicillin. Getting in touch with Fleming, Florey and Chain consulted with him and enlisted his aid and advice. Florey and Chain painstakingly experimented with methods of securing enough penicillin to use in laboratory experiments. That done, they confirmed Fleming's findings that penicillin indeed did kill staph, strep, and pneumo germs.

Like Fleming, the two young scientists were unable to filtrate enough pure penicillin to perform large-scale experiments. On February 12, 1941, when the two had just enough penicillin for use on a single patient, they learned that a policeman was critically ill in the Oxford Radcliffe Hospital. His condition was serious, the prognosis hopeless, because even the newly discovered sulfa drugs had been ineffectual in his treatment. In a desperate effort, the precious penicillin was used on the policeman. Florey and Chain allowed the drug to drip into the man's arm through a hypodermic needle inserted into his vein. The victim's fever went down, and his festered sores improved. On the fifth day of treatment, the last drop of penicillin was used up. There was no more of the drug. Swiftly, the patient's temperature rose, and soon he died.

Florey and Chain extracted more penicillin in pure form but in inadequate amounts. They encountered other bitter experiences with patients when the drug supply was exhausted. They also had some successes, but those were few.

Obviously, the major problem of penicillin production remained the same as when Fleming made the original discovery. It could not be produced in the medical research laboratory. Mass manufacture of it had somehow to be achieved. In 1941, the Rockefeller Institute of Medical Research provided funds for Florey to go to the United States in the hope that American aid could be found for production of penicillin on a commercial basis. Finally, in 1943, American pharmaceutical companies, with the sanction of the United States War Production Board, mass-produced the drug, with the agreement that it be used only for treatment of soldiers in the Allied armies. Within a little more than a year, penicillin was being made in such vast quantities that the War Production Board's limitation was lifted and the drug made available to civilians.

Today penicillin combats certain complications of the common cold, some types of pneumonia and heart diseases, various infectious diseases, syphilis, gonorrhea, and is used in the treatment of burns, boils, carbuncles, and other infected sores and wounds of many kinds. Every year hundreds of thousands of people survive who would have died without the efficacious drug penicillin; millions quickly recover from minor and major ailments treated with penicillin.

The three scientists shared the Nobel prize in 1945 "for the discovery of penicillin and its therapeutic effect for the cure of different infectious maladies." Fleming and Florey, both born British subjects, were also knighted for their contributions to medicine. Sir Alexander Fleming died in 1955; Sir Howard Florey still carries on his investigations at Queen's College, Oxford University. Ernst Boris Chain is chairman of the Department of Biochemistry at the Imperial College of Sciences in London.

Who Will Save
Lives Tomorrow?

Medical achievements of any age are dependent on past progress, those of today are based on concepts, theories, techniques, and methods of yesterday and the millennia preceding it. Tomorrow's breakthroughs will result from research dating back to ancient times and from the interdependence of scientific disciplines that is a present-day orientation.

In the sixteenth century, Fracastoro said that "all things are related in some way, one to the other. To gain understanding, we must learn many subjects and find the point where each crosses the other." The juxtaposition of pathology, virology, and neurology with atomic chemistry and electronics could only be realized in this century. We once presented experts in those five fields on a nationally televised program entitled *Where Did It Begin?*

Scientists representing the specific disciplines traced through many centuries the scientific discoveries that affect medicine today, at the "point where each crosses the other," still sometimes only tenuously. The guests, one after another, linked the past with the present:

The atomic chemist, reviewing the value of nuclear energy, named the radiations that alleviate suffering and touched on the potential of those rays for medical cure. He capsuled the history of his field, tracing its course from ancient Greece and the word *atom,* has been adopted into our language. Thousands of years of research by men of wisdom and dedication preceded the success of Enrico Fermi in splitting the atom and creating the self-sustaining fission uranium; Fermi duly credited the legions of predecessors who made possible his achievement, which won for him the Nobel prize.

The pathologist outlined many diseases that have been known for millennia: tuberculosis, mentioned in Egyptian hieroglyphics; typhoid fever, described by four physicians of ancient Greece; typhus, amazingly defined in a Sumerian book of medicine; the treatment for diabetes administered by a Roman court doctor; and stomach ulcers, studied by an Assyrian priest-physician. The doctor rapidly illustrated how the path of discovery and development winds from ancient times to modern until one man or one team reaches the medical goal.

The electronics specialist discussed electronics in medicine, a provocative new area of research, diagnosis, and therapy. With drawings and photographs, he demonstrated how Thales of Miletus, a Greek philosopher, observed the property of static electricity in 602 B.C.; he read from Aristotle about the "torpedo fish [electric ray fish] that narcotizes the creatures it wants to catch . . . the torpedo's shock I have experienced with my own self-inflicted experiments"; and he discussed William Gilbert's work with electricity. In 1600 Gilbert revealed that the secret of electricity is friction and named the phenomenon from the Greek word *electron,* meaning amber, the substance observed by Thales. The detailed development of medical applications of electronics encompassed German research of the mid-seventeenth century; British, in the mid-eighteenth century, and also included the contributions of John Walsh, Benjamin Franklin, Luigi Galvani, and Alessandro Volta. With apparatus in the television studio, our guest demonstrated how the *electroencephalograph* examines the brain, and the *electrocardiograph,* the cardiovascular system; these medical electronic machines and others would not have been possible had not many men since Thales of Greece conducted experimental work on the phenomenon.

The neurologist traced the development of his specialty, beginning with the writings of Hippocrates on the subject of apoplexy and the treatment of mental disorders in the hospital of Aesculapius at Epidaurus in ancient Greece; he discussed the Aristotelian concepts of the form and function of the brain advanced in later centuries by such neurologists as David Ferrier and Harvey Cushing.

The virologist highlighted the studies of vaccines, immunology, and antitoxins made in ancient times and by Fracastoro, Paracelsus, Edward Jenner, Virchow, Louis Pasteur, Kocher, Ehrlich, and Fleming; he included facts about the sulfa drug first discovered by the Austrian chemist Paul Glemo in 1908 and the production of synthetic sulfas by E. A. Bliss, E. K. Marshall, and P. H. Long in the United States.

The television program's emphasis on the importance of both fundamental and applied research had its impact on a friend who said to us, a day or so later, "You know, I never thought of it before I saw that show, but a heck of a lot of men have to do plenty of work for a long time before one scientist can announce that he has discovered something. He doesn't do it all alone or all of a sudden." How right he was. And no great medical scientist ever claims a discovery for himself alone.

Dr. Jonas Salk received a Nobel prize for his poliomyelitis vaccine, but he has stressed again and again his dependence on earlier research by others. After the announcement of his great discovery, Salk, in articles, at news conferences, and in public lectures, gave full credit, often by name, to contemporary investigators whose research helped him to find the substance that produced immunity against polio. They and he owe debts, and acknowledge them, to numerous scientists who, through the years, doggedly investigated the subject of immunology, making possible the Salk vaccine, quite properly named in recognition of its discoverer. Statistics of the decade following the discovery give evidence of its great contribution to mankind: There were 18,000 cases of paralytic polio in 1954; only 94 cases were recorded in 1964.

With every advance so revolutionary, hope rises for the discovery of therapy and cure for other devastating ailments. The diseases that accounted for 71 percent of deaths in the United States one recent year were cancer and heart diseases. Cancer took the lives of 277,110 people that year; 832,200 patients were under treatment for some form of cancer and 540,000, or more than half of those, were new cases. In the same year 954,870 people died from some cardiovascular disease. More than 2 million people were diagnosed as having a heart disease, and over 200,000 people died from stroke, a cardiovascular disease that has a survival record of eight out of every ten.

These killers and cripplers will be conquered as a result of medical research, which today is moving forward with incredible rapidity. For instance, it was stated in a National Institutes of Health report that "seventy-five percent of the drugs used in hospitals today were not even known ten years ago." Procedures in operations and techniques of therapy are advancing with proportionate speed. One reason for this acceleration is that there are more scientists living and working today in laboratories than lived and worked in the entire time from Hippocrates to the beginning of the twentieth century. Also, all branches of science have reached a high degree of sophistication, with so much knowledge available and so many pieces of refined equipment at hand that discovery and application can be measured in months rather than by the decade.

There is general awareness of the value and extent of contemporary scientific research and a willingness to support it in every way possible. Financial support is obtained through fund drives among private citizens; from foundations created by the wealthy; from grants—commercial, industrial, individual, and governmental. The researcher with a worthy project is able today to obtain funds, laboratory space, equipment, and cooperation.

In thousands of laboratories the world over, research experts are searching for the causes of diseases, the methods for alleviating them, the techniques for checking the now incurable ravages against man, and the therapy for arresting conditions before they become virulent. Teams representative of many scientific disciplines are delving into the past for clues to medical mysteries, cooperating on theories that may lead to future progress.

Since a "lot of men have to do plenty of work for a long time before one scientist can announce that he has discovered something," lives tomorrow will be saved through contributions made by scientists prominent in medical history of the past and outstanding in the medical profession today.

Index